TABLE OF CONTENTS

Why Learn About World War I

The Great War of 1914-1918 changed the world forever. Four large empires, the German,* Austrian-Hungarian, Russian and Ottoman, were broken up. *(See glossary for German Empire.) More than 20 small nations were created from them. New weapons of war were introduced that were more destructive than could have been imagined. These weapons were used with such efficiency that the deaths of over nine million soldiers on both sides created the largest loss of life in history due to war. In addition, at least 15 million civilians died from fighting, bombing, disease and starvation.

The war started when Austria took revenge for the assassination of its Archduke Ferdinand and his wife while making an official visit in Sarajevo, a city in Bosnia. The assassin was a Serbian, a member of

Map of Europe alliances - 1914

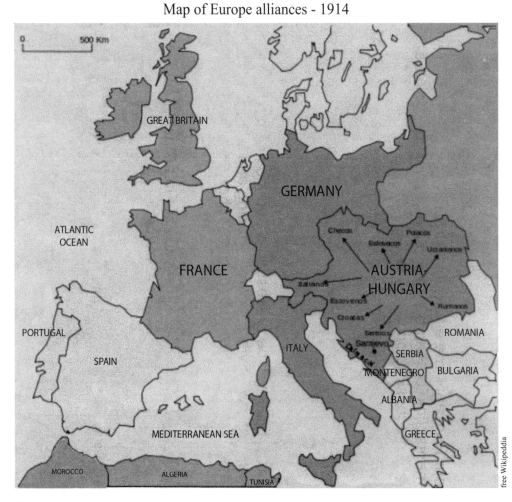

a the Black Hand nationalist group. A few days after Austria declared war on Serbia, Germany declared war on Russia. Within days France, Britain and Belgium became participants in what was becoming a world war.

Many changes took place, personally and politically in the world. The role of women changed drastically, as many women had to replace men's jobs in factories and on farms. In Russia, revolutionaries overthrew the czar and ended the 300 year Romanov monarchy. A brand new form of government, Communism, then emerged from Russia's brutal civil war. Most important for Americans was the beginning of the United States' rise as the world's super power.

This book was written for adults and children to explore together many important topics of World War I. Together they can begin to understand the tragedy and suffering of soldiers and civilians who lived during these difficult times.

Some stories tell of personal victories. Other stories reveal the lasting relationships of soldiers with animals, such as dogs, horses and pigeons. These tales of heroism show the endurance of human and animal spirit.

This Great War was not the "war to end all wars," as people hoped for at the time. In reality, the harsh terms of the peace settlement laid the foundation for World War II, only 20 years later.

The author hopes that readers will learn lessons from World War I encouraging them to seek peaceful ways to end disputes and disagreements.

Then this will be the "War That Ends All Wars."

Nancy Cramer
September, 2012
Raymore, Missouri

1870 - **French emperor Napoleon III unwisely declared war on Germany, which defeated France quickly at the battle of Sedan, leaving France greatly humiliated and wanting to take revenge.**

1912 - **First of two short Balkan wars in which the Turks were defeated by a group of Balkan countries, including Serbia and Bulgaria. They gained some new territories.**

1913 - **The second Balkan war where Serbia defeated Bulgaria which wanted more land than given the year before. Serbia also took control of Albania but was forced by Austria to return it to Austria.**

1914

June 28	Austrian Archduke Francis Ferdinand and his wife are assassinated in Sarajevo.
July 28	Austria declares war on Serbia.
August 1	Germany declares war on Russia.
August 3	Germany declares war on France.
August 4	Germany invades Belgium, a neutral country; Great Britain declares war on Germany.
August	Russians defeated by Germans at Battle of Tannenberg on Eastern Front; 90,000 Russian prisoners are taken; big morale boost for Germans.
September 5-12	First Battle of the Marne (River) - terrible losses on both sides.
October 29	Turkey (old Ottoman Empire) enters war on Germany's side.
By end of year	German drive stopped 25 miles from Paris; trench warfare begins 1915.

1914   1915

1915

January 19	Germany launches first Zeppelin raid on London.
February 4	Germans begin submarine warfare against merchant ships.
April-May	Germans use poison gas at second Battle of Ypres.
May 7	German submarine sinks the Lusitania with 1,198 lives lost including 128 Americans.
By September 6	Germans and Austrians conquer Poland and Lithuania; Russians lose nearly two million men (dead, wounded, taken prisoner).
October 6	Germany, Austria-Hungary and Bulgaria invade Serbia.
November 27	Serbian army collapses. Serbian army and thousands of civilians have begun retreat to safety across mountains of Albania. Thousands die of hunger, disease, enemy and bandit attacks, cold weather and exhaustion.

1916

January 9	Allies suffer large defeat by Ottoman Turks at Gallipoli.
January 27	The draft is introduced in Great Britain.
February 21	Beginning of Battle of Verdun, in which French lose almost 350,000 men and British lose 200,000.

1916   1917

July-November	Battle of the Somme-British suffer 60,000 dead or wounded the first day (worst in British fighting history) for a battle total of 400,000; French lose 200,000; and Germans, 450,000. No clear win for either side.
September 15	British at the Somme River area used armored tanks for first time in history.

1917

January 16	Telegram sent to Mexico by Arthur Zimmerman, German official, asking Mexico to become German ally. When telegram is published, Americans reacted strongly.
February 1	Germany again starts unrestricted submarine warfare.
April 6	America declares war on Germany.
June 25	Small group of American troops land in France; too few in numbers to begin fighting.
October-Dec.	Battle of Caporetto River in which Italians fight desperately against Austrians, but lose 600,000 troops as prisoners or deserters.
December 23	Russia's new Bolshevik government signs Armistice with Germany, making Russia out of the war now. Czar had abdicated in March. He and his family were assassinated July 16, 1918.

1918

March-June	Germans make strong offensive attacks. Spanish flu cases appear in the United States for the first time.

1918   1919

April-May	Thousands of French troops mutiny because of lack of food, bad fighting conditions and great losses due to poor command decisions made at recent battles of Arras and Vimy Ridge; General Petain takes over command and settles mutiny, creating better situations; many punished as result.
June	Americans' first important battle at Chateau-Thierry made by Marines halting German advance.
July 15-Aug. 5	Second battle of the Marne; beginning of collapse of German army.
September	Second wave of Spanish flu begins in United States, spreads to Europe and around the world.
September-Oct.	Allies' battles at Amiens, St. Mihiel, Argonne (Forest) and Ypres.
October 29	German navy begins to mutiny.
November	German Kaiser abdicates.
November 11	Armistice signed at 11a.m.; fighting stops on Western Front.
November	Third wave of Spanish flu hits United States. Worldwide estimates of between 50,000,000 and 130,000,000 persons died, making it one of the most deadly disasters in human history.

1919

Troops in the trenches with gas masks

May 7-June 28	Peace Treaty of Versailles is written and Germans and Allies sign it. The War is officially ended.

NWWI museum archives, Kansas City, MO

CAUSES AND WORLD EVENTS
How World War I Began

"Good morning, class," Ms. Browning said as the students took their seats. "We are going to begin a unit on one of the most important events in the 20th century, and perhaps in all recorded history. This event took place only about 100 years ago, however, I want you to understand why it is considered so important to us today. This event is World War I, often referred to as "The Great War," or, "The War That Ended All Wars.""

"The war began in August, 1914 when Austria-Hungary declared war against Serbia. Take out the timeline so we can refer to it. Now what are some reasons nations go to war?" Ms. Browning paused as the students looked at the timeline.

Jose raised his hand. "Sometimes it's for more land, or it can be revenge, to punish another country for something bad that happened. More land was why we had many wars with the American Indians, and of course, they fought back to defend themselves. But our Indians believed the land belonged to everyone. I don't think in Europe people believed that way."

Ms. Browning said, "You are correct in both reasons. The Germans wanted overseas possessions, or colonies as they were called, just like the French and British had. Also the Germans wanted the raw materials those colonies produced. The Germans in 1871 took part of France to obtain the valuable coal mines there. What do you think the French reaction was?" Dustin raised his hand. "Well, I bet they were mad about it and wanted to punish the Germans. But the French didn't start the war, Germany did."

Ms. Browning agreed, "So, let's read on about the other reasons. Read silently the next paragraph and someone answer." The class read silently: "One reason the war began so quickly was all the alliances and treaties the countries had with each other. Austria-Hungary had a treaty with Germany. France had one with Russia. All the countries had a treaty with Belgium. That was because when it was founded as an independence country in 1831, it was declared a neutral country. A neutral country is one that would not go to war.

The European powers all agreed, and the Treaty of London was signed."

Cathi asked, "What are alliances, Ms. Browning?"

The teacher asked for a definition. No response, then reluctantly, Wesley raised his hand, looking at the two boys who usually snickered when he answered. They were reading the handout and didn't look up. "Well, an alliance is like when you make a promise, or an agreement between people, or between several nations. Then you become allies. Just like computer games about allies."

Ms. Browning nodded and said, "You explained it well, Wesley. And you also used the word 'Allies,' which is the name used by France, Britain, Belgium and Russia. Once the war started, more than 20 more countries joined them. This included the United States. In international law, an alliance or treaty is a formal obligation. The honor of the country depends upon how well they keep the treaties they make. Now, read the next two paragraphs." The students read silently:

"Because some of the countries had developed the technology to make weapons, they made large numbers of them, such as guns, especially machine guns and heavy artillery.

"They could equip large armies, so they recruited and trained thousands of soldiers. This was true of Germany more than any other nation. They had the largest standing army in the world, except perhaps the Russians, who usually depended upon recruiting peasants in time of need. Both armies consisted of four million soldiers each. The French had 3.8 million, and the British only 190,000 professional soldiers." Ms. Browning asked, "What is meant by 'technology?' "

Josip raised his hand. "It means they, people, know how to make things using machines and not by hand." Ms. Browning nodded her head, then asked, "Do the sizes of the various armies give you any clues about the beginning of the war?" DaVonda answered, "I think it means that some nations were prepared for war, and maybe even wanted to go to war. I would have thought the British had more soldiers than that." "Who wants to comment on DaVonda's statement?" Ms. Browning questioned. "Well, I think it was because Britain had such a large navy," Micky began, "and maybe they thought their navy would protect them. After all, they are an island country and not part of the European continent. So maybe they thought they were finished fighting wars in Europe."

Ms. Browning nodded and pulled her power point cart over. "Let's look at the European continent and find out where some of the countries are that took part in the war." With her pointer she indicated Serbia. "Here is the small country of Serbia in southern Europe. For hundreds of years Serbia had been subjected to the harsh rule of the Ottoman Empire. All these other lands also belonged to the Ottoman Empire." She indicated Bulgaria, Romania, Croatia, Albania and Montenegro. "What was the Ottoman Empire? That's a name no longer used."

Chris explained, "It was a huge Muslim empire that at one time ruled a great deal of land both in Europe and in what we call the Middle East. Also some countries in the north part of Africa."

"Very good, Chris, I see you are interested in this area. Let's read about Serbia in the next two paragraphs" and the students silently read:

"The Serbs wanted to have their own empire again. They lost it in the 1400s when they were conquered by the Ottomans. The Serbs fought two brief wars for independence, one in 1912 and another one in 1913. By joining with some small neighboring countries, the Serbs defeated the Ottomans. The Ottomans had to retreat all the way back to Istanbul, their capital.

"But in 1913 the Bulgarians attacked Serbia because they wanted more land than had been given them in 1912. The Serbians defeated the Bulgarians. They had once been allies. The victorious Serbs seized the coastal land of Albania. This finally gave Serbia access to sea ports. By now, however, Austria-Hungary had assembled and equipped their huge army and gave Serbia an ultimatum. 'Give up

Albania in eight days or else.' So Serbian soldiers left Albania. They still had the other land they had won, but not an access to the sea. None of the countries were satisfied and all were full of resentments and anger."

Ms. Browning, holding out her pointer, said, "Someone come up and show where Albania and Bulgaria are so we can see why with their position, they were in conflict with Albania." Tricia volunteered and indicated the countries. "Who can summarize the reasons the countries were resentful?" Ms. Browning asked.

Ray spoke up. "Well, France wanted that Alsace-something that Germany had taken. Serbia wanted Albania, Austria-something told them to give it back. Maybe Austria wanted Albania for itself becase they had no seacoast. And Bulgaria wanted more land because it didn't get enough in the first war."

"Good, now we have the right recipe for another war. All we lack is a catalyst, a spark, something that finally sets it all off," Ms. Browning summarized. "Read the next several paragraphs to find out what was the spark." The students read:

"On June 1914, a young member of the Black Hand, a nationalist group from Serbia, made a drastic move on his part. This started the fateful events that happened quickly. Once these events took place, there was no stopping the process to war. This is the story. The Archduke Franz Ferdinand, nephew of the Austrian Emperor, and his wife, Sophia, were making a royal visit to several cities. The morning of June 28,1914 they came to the city of Sarajevo in Bosnia-Herzegovina, a neighboring province to Serbia. After making several official stops along the route, the chauffeur accidentally turned the wrong way.

"This provided the opportunity the young man, Gavarilo Princep, had been waiting for. He and several other members of the Black Hand had stationed themselves along the route with pistols, bombs and poison tablets to swallow if caught. The open touring car made an unexpected stop in front of Princip. Here was his chance. He quickly fired two shots point blank at the Archduke and his wife, killing both. Princip was caught by bystanders before he could take the poison. He was imprisoned immediately and died in prison several years later of tuberculosis. He had hoped to die as a hero for the Serbian cause, but his death was just one of the more than nine million soldiers who died in four years of fighting."

Several students looked at each other not believing what they had read. They whispered questions, one girl shaking her head, another one nodding in agreement. They continued reading: "Europe was in a state of shock. In response, Austria gave demands to Serbia that were so severe Serbia could not possibly agree to.

"These demands included that Serbia would condemn any military involvement with the murders; have no further anti-Austrian intrigue; and Austria would join in with the search for the murderers and in setting their punishment. In other words, Austria would interfere with Serbian justice and courts. These were just part of the 15 demands and were totally unacceptable to any sovereign nation.

"As a result, within days war was declared between the two countries. The next country to get involved in the war was Russia. Russia had a treaty with Serbia, because both nations were of ethnic Slavic background. So Russia announced it was going to mobilize, that is, get its army prepared for war.

"A day later, Germany declared war on Russia and two days after that, Germany declared war on France. However, it was the large, powerful nation of Russia that Germany actually feared. Russia had recently taken over some smaller countries, and Germany feared Russia might try to seize some German territory."

Ms. Browning asked, "Germany had a well trained army of 4,000,000 men. Russia also had the same number of men, even more when peasants were called to arms. But Russians were not well trained and especially lacked even basic equipment such as rifles." Chris remarked," my great-grandparents came from Russia in early 1900s, and they talked about how backward Russia was in so many ways. Their families had been serfs and could not go to school until the czar freed the serfs. By then, they were too old to go to school. Besides, my great-grandparents lived out in the countryside on large manors and there were no schools nearby. They wanted their children to be educated and that's one reason they came to America. Another reason was they were afraid.

"My family is of Jewish background, and the czar often sent soldiers, Cossacks, into the villages to scare and even kill them. There was plenty of good farm land and lots of people, but most were ignorant and uneducated. They would not make good soldiers until they had been trained." He stopped, his face flushed with emotion. "Hmm, very interesting, Chris. You have a lot of information about your family, and you are right about conditions in Russia for the common people. Thank you for telling us." Ms. Browning told the class to continue reading silently. They read:

"Germany had planned to attack France and get to Paris in six weeks, thereby taking France out of the war. Germany could then turn its attention to its eastern front and the threat of Russian invasion. To do this, Germany planned to invade its small northern neighbor, the neutral country of Belgium. By crossing its borders, the road to Paris was a faster route.

"But when Germany invaded Belgium, ignoring its neutrality, the invasion plans were halted. To everyone's surprise, the small Belgian army put up a strong defense. King Albert, the reigning monarch, himself led the army. He ordered the sea dykes be opened. The fields were then flooded with several feet of sea water, almost stopping German progress.

"This slowed down the German advance for a week. This gave Great Britain time to transport its already organized small professional army across the English Channel to help defend Belgium. Thereby Great Britain honored its treaty to defend Belgium. More countries joined the war, either with the Allies, or the Central Powers.

"Europe went to war in a little over one month after the Archduke was killed." Ms. Browning commented as she noticed that most her students had raised their hands, indicating they had finished reading.

"Now, students, what do you understand as the reasons the

war was started in Europe. I will list them on the board, and you copy them for later use. What was one of the first reasons? Remember there were many. Let's try to list them in the order they occurred. So number one was?" She paused and asked Brent.

He responded, "I think it was more land and power." Ms. Browning wrote, "Desire for more land (colonies) and power. Right. Next, Claudia?" The teacher had seen Claudia's waving hand. "Large armies and improvement in technology of weapons," Claudia answered without hesitation. Ms. Browning wrote the responses on the board. "You are doing fine. Now what were other causes?"

"I think it was making treaties or alliances," Josip answered. "But, when were these all made? I don't think it could have happened fast, because treaties are complicated." "You are right, Josip. Many of these treaties had been made years before. It does take a long time to agree on a treaty. Why do you think that is?"

Josip began slowly, "Well, you want to be sure you can still agree with it a long time from now. You might get into a fight – uh war, and be sorry you made the agreement. Besides, it has to be made by several people and sometimes even a lot more people have to agree with it."

"Correct, again, Josip. Now what was the incident that sparked or started all this?" Many hands were raised. "Candi, what do you remember?" "It was the killing of the king or prince or somebody from Austria by a terrorist from Serbia, I think it

Elaborate systems of trenches faced each other along the Western and Eastern Fronts.

NWWI museum archives, Kansas City, MO

is called," Candi replied.

"You're on the right track. Larry can you tell us more?" Ms. Browning asked. Larry patiently began, "Well, it was the Archduke, and he was the son of the Emperor of the Austria-Hungarian Empire. That's what 'heir' means. And the booklet didn't say 'terrorist,' although today probably the TV announcers might use that word. The killing is called an 'assassination,' which means to plan to kill some one, like our President Lincoln and President Kennedy were killed. I hope no one has any plans today to kill the president we have today," he said, then added, "The killings took place in Bosnia-Herzegovina, and the assassin was from Serbia. That's how Serbia became blamed."

"Very good job of summarizing, and we all share your hope about our president," Ms. Browning replied. "Class time is up. Put your list in a safe place. You have your notes from yesterday and today to study later for a test. They will also be useful for a short paper you are going to write. Many of these reasons are the same reasons why wars have started at various places and times in history.

"But, remember, this war is very special. It is the pivotal point of 20th century history. 'Pivotal' is a word we will explore later. Dismissed." Ms. Browning finished just before the bell rang. The students gathered their books and left.

"I wonder if these lessons will make any impact on my students. They are so young, and this is such a serious topic. Well, guess I'll find out," she sighed, as the next class of students came in the door, laughing and talking.

New Zealand transport on the Amiens-Albert Road, September 1916.

Q1352 Crown Copyright by permission of The Imperial War Museums

"Please take out the handouts we read yesterday," Ms. Browning said bringing her class to order. Students stopped talking and started searching their notebooks. "Let's review our topic from yesterday. Who wants to start?" Ms. Browning asked.

Su Lyn answered, "We learned how the war started in Europe. There were a lot of reasons, including the assassination of the son of an emperor, of Austria, I think."

"Very good, other reasons?" Ms. Browning probed. Dwon began, "Desire for land, Serbian wars, large armies, alliances and treaties. This was real interesting. I've always wondered about why wars are started. Seems like two reasons are always about land and money. Power too," he concluded.

Ms. Browning smiled, "You've saved us a lot of time, Dwon, by listing and summarizing. Let's go on with our reading today, and see if any of these reasons were why the United States entered the war. We will take turns reading out loud for a while. Who wants to be first?"

Franco volunteered and began to read slowly, "He kept us out of war. For over two and one-half years, President Wilson and Congress kept the United States out of World War I." He paused and looked at his teacher. She nodded approval, and asked, "Why would that be important?"

Dustin raised his hand and began, "Well, I think it was because war is a terrible thing. Our country knew what war was like when we had the Civil War, and last semester we learned how it almost destroyed the South and killed thousands of soldiers. Guess people now didn't want to get killed."

Ms. Browning smiled at his answer. "Yes, you were very interested in the war and the huge number of casualties. People remembered this, and they didn't want to fight a war again and have a large loss of lives. They knew about the large number of casualties because they read about it in the newspapers although sometimes the British and French governments didn't want to stress their losses. They emphasized the German and Austrian deaths. In 1917, after almost three years, there were nearly six million deaths for all the armies. Tricia, please read the next paragraph."

Tricia looked up when her name was called. She quickly read, "From the start of the war, America was supplying Great Britain and France with food, horses, mules, raw materials and military items. In addition they were loaning a lot of money in the form of bonds. It was such a large amount that if the Germans won, the United States economy would be badly affected. So it was important for America to do all she could to help the Allies win. Then there is the disaster of the passenger ship, 'Lus-i-tan-i-a.' Is that how it is pronounced?"

"Yes, that is correct. Please continue," Ms. Browning said. Tricia read, "When the British passenger ship, 'Lus-i-tan-ia' was torpedoed in 1915 by a German submarine, 128 American lives were lost in the sinking of the ship. This made some Americans angry, and some thought America would declare war on Germany then. But most Americans still thought the war was Europe's war. This type of thinking is called 'i-so-la-tion-ism'" She paused. "What does that mean, and why didn't they declare war? After all, those who died on the ship were innocent civilians, not soldiers," Tricia protested.

"First, let's discuss the phrase 'Europe's war.' What do you think it means?" asked Ms. Browning. Almost everyone raised their hands. Juan answered, "It means the war began in Europe, and only European countries were involved."

"Yes, that's correct. Now to Tricia's second question. It is more complicated and was the same question many Americans were asking each other. Why didn't President Wilson declare war on Germany? Read on, please, Su Lyn, and see what the answer is."

Su Lyn began, "President Wilson had to consider several more issues when deciding to lead the United States into war. First, he had campaigned on the slogan, 'He kept us out of war.' He just barely won the election in 1916. The vote was close. People might think he was breaking his promise. Second, there were over ten million immigrants from Germany and Austria in the United States.

"This country had about 90 million total population then. That means those immigrants made up more than 10% of our population. He was afraid they might be persecuted or harassed. And he was right. There were riots, violence and intimidation against them. Many immigrants even changed their last names to something that sounded more English," Su Lyn paused.

Ms. Browning smiled as she saw her students starting to think about what Su Lyn had just read. "What do you think about having to change your name to escape being bullied or beaten? How many of you would do it?" The students looked at each other, then hands slowly began to rise. About half the class indicated "Yes."

Ms. Browning continued, "How were you feeling when you thought you might have to change your name to be safe? Do you think this is the American way to treat people?" Micky raised his hand. "No, of course not. Everyone here is supposed to be equal and be treated with justice. But, Ms. Browning, you know there are bullies around, and people are just people. Sometimes they don't act right." Micky looked around to see if others were agreeing with him. He saw some nod their heads, and this made him continue.

"If I saw someone beating up on someone else, I'd try to make him stop. Unless he was really a lot bigger than I am. Then I'd be a little scared, and I'm not sure what I would do," Micky admitted.

Ms. Browning said, "That is brave of you to say that, Micky, because that did happen many times. That made President Wilson think twice, maybe even three or four times about declaring war on Germany and the other Central Powers because we had immigrants from those countries. We have to be aware of his background. He was the son of a Presbyterian minister and the grandson of a pastor.

"Possibly this influenced his way of thinking as did his career as a history professor. He learned from teaching and reading history how men have started wars. Also what were the consequences. Later he was selected to be president of Princeton University. Then in 1912 he was elected to his first term as president of the United States. So he was influenced by many factors. Now, who wants to read next?"

Darlene raised her hand. She loved to read out loud and had

good pronounciation and a good sense of word meanings. In her heart she secretly wanted to become an actor. "In 1917 Germany took a GREAT risk when they declared the start of unannounced submarine attacks AGAIN. All ships, even neutral ones, when they were in certain waters would be attacked. The United States had QUIETLY begun preparation for undeclared war by arming merchant marine ships. Gun crews were trained in defense against the U-boats, as German submarines were called." She looked up and smiled as she finished. Two boys whispered to each other and snickered. Ms. Browning looked in their direction with a frown. They quickly stopped and pretended to be paying attention.

"Good, Darlene. The nickname 'U-boats' comes from an abbreviation of the German word, 'Unterseesboot', meaning 'under water boat.' Now what were unannounced submarine attacks? And why is that important?" Ms. Browning asked.

Ray raised his hand. "Well, 'unannounced' means you don't announce you are going to torpedo a ship. You just go ahead and shoot the ship you see in the periscope without bothering to find out what country it's from and what kind of ship it is, passenger or cargo." He continued, "If you knew in advance about the attack, you would get off the ship, maybe, or fire some guns or something. Couldn't they radio for help?"

Ms. Browning responded. "You have to remember how primitive radios were in those days, although they did have wireless using Morse code. So calling for help was limited. But one thing the story didn't say was that after the sinking of the 'Lusitania,' Germany agreed to announce an attack when it came upon a ship. This would give the crews time to get away in life boats. Even then, sometimes sailors died or were taken prisoner by the Germans. The cold Atlantic waters were hazardous for those in life boats, and rescue by Allied ships might take several days.

"But also consider the valuable cargo the ships were carrying, and how necessary it was for the English or French to get delivery. At times they were almost desperate for the food and supplies. And of course, the merchants and ship owners wanted their ships safe from attack. But despite this, the Germans continued the attacks," Ms. Browning finished. "Next reader?" Ms. Browning looked around the classroom. Dustin raised his hand and began reading:

"Then the Germans took another risk when they sent a telegram to the German ambassador in Mexico. The telegram told of plans to ask the Mexicans to join in a fight against America. This way the Mexicans could regain the area of Texas, New Mexico and other parts they lost to the United States years ago. This telegram was intercepted by the British and decoded. Because the telegram was sent by the German head of foreign ministry, Arthur Zimmermann, it has become known as the 'Zimmermann telegram.'

"In the meantime the Germans announced starting unannounced submarine warfare again. This time the Congress was furious, and some leaders called for President Wilson to declare war. At this time, however, still no one except the British Royal Navy intelligence service knew about the telegram and its contents. On February 26, 1917 President Wilson, unaware of the telegram, asked Congress for approval to arm American merchant marine ships with guns. The approval was not granted. Still Congress continued to argue about approval, not knowing about the secret telegram. However, two days later the Secretary of State Lansing was given the telegram. He immediately sent it to the President and on that day, the message were released to the press.

"It was so astonishing that many people refused to believe it was true. About three weeks later, after three more American ships were sunk by German submarines, President Wilson asked Congress to declare war against Germany. He received overwhelming approval this time. On April 6 the United States finally was at war. In President Wilson's famous words, 'The world must be made safe for democracy.'

"What a shock it must have been to our government when they learned about Germany's effort to involve our neighbor, Mexico," Claudia said, then asked, "But, Ms. Browning, how could the Germans think that America would let the sinking of ships go on?"

"If we think about the word 'isolationism,' this may help us to understand how the Germans thought. They had sunk many, many ships and America did nothing about them. They had brutally mistreated the Belgian people and destroyed such important buildings as the University in Louvain which held hundreds of rare medieval manuscripts. These were burned deliberately. Innocent civilians were rounded up and shot for no reason except reprisal, that is revenge. Still the United States had said or done nothing. So maybe that is why the Germans continued these acts."

Ms. Browning took a deep breath and looked for a reaction from her students. Most of this information was new to them, but she decided it was time to reveal more of the atrocities committed by the Germans and other Central Powers countries. The students reacted as she had anticipated. Disbelief. Could it be true? Did armies behave in this manner?

To her relief, she saw Wesley's hand. He rarely volunteered. "I think I understand what you mean. The Central Powers thought America would continue to do nothing, and then with the shipping badly destroyed, France and England would have to surrender. The Russians were out of the war by then because of their revolution, so the whole German and Austrian armies could be sent to the western front. German forces would be superior then. But, Ms. Browning, I wonder, did any of the congressmen regret that by delaying declaration of war, so many more lives would be lost both at sea and on land. On land because of lack of supplies and ammunition. Did they ever think of that?"

"I don't know, Wesley, it is something to think about. When does a nation have to take a stand in the case of declaring war? Having the right to decide is a privilege of being a democracy. But there is also a responsibility that goes with it. We have just 15 minutes of class time left. Just enough for each of you to write your position on isolationism. Was it the right thing for America to stay out of the war until 1917, or should we have declared war sooner? Just write your opinion, with your reasons for thinking so. Any questions?" Ms. Browning asked.

Earlier in the unit, Ms. Browning had passed out some of extra credit work. "These are slang words used by soldiers in World War I. They are underlined, and the definitions can be found in the Glossary. On the second page, fill in the meaning you find. See if you can guess what the slang means and what words we use today to mean the same thing. This will be due the end of the unit. Now today's class..."

A Yank and a Tommy are talking. What are they saying?

YANK - I like your "the rain in face" and "your red legs."
TOMMY - Yep, it keeps the sun off and they're good for my "undercarriage" .You "rookies" kept "Fritz" and his "typewriters" busy yesterday. I fancy your "tin Lizzie." By the way, you got any extra "tin cows" for my "bully beef?"
YANK - My "top" may have some, but he gets "ticked off toot pronto." Us "doughboys" like "deep sea turkey" with some "red lead."
TOMMY - Jolly good, our "Archibalds" did a "boocoo" job on "Fritz" and his "wurst" yesterday. His "ashcans" sounded like "Big Bertha" at first.
YANK - Yeah, I was in my "pup tent" when the "ammo" truck came. The "top" came and I had to "pump handle" mighty fast. I lost my "monkey cap" in the hurry to get away from the "aerial torpedoes".
TOMMY - How'd you like the way our "ack ack" did a job on the "Boche's "Kite Balloons" too?
YANK - Yeah, fine show, then we had to "stand to" after it was over. I was sure the "Alleymen" would attack with their "stick bombs" and I'd get a "Blighty One."
TOMMY - Got any leftover "deep sea turkey?" I'm awful hungry. Those "dog biscuits" and "gold fish" are bad. Our gang's been counting the "flying bedsteads" and "galloping geese" in our sector. You seen any?
YANK - No, hey, there's the "bevo" and I gotta "pump handle" again.

ANSWERS TO "What are they saying?"

A Yank and a Tommy are talking. What are they saying?

YANK - I like your _____ and _____ .

TOMMY - Yep, it keeps the sun off and they're good for

my _____ You _____ kept _____ and his

_____ busy yesterday.

I fancy your _____ By the way, got any

extra _____ for my _____ ?

YANK - My _____ may have some but he gets _____

_____ . Us _____

like _____ with some _____ .

TOMMY - Jolly good, our _____ did a _____ job

on _____ and his _____ yesterday.

His _____ sounded like _____ at first.

YANK - Yeah, I was in my _____ when the _____

truck came. The _____ came and I had to _____

mighty fast. I lost my _____ in the hurry to get

away from the _____ .

TOMMY - How'd you like the way our _____ did a job on

the _____ _____ too?

YANK - Yeah, fine show. Then we had to _____

after it was over. I was sure the _____ would attack

with their _____ and I'd get a _____ .

TOMMY - Got any left over _____ ? I'm awful hungry.

Those _____ and _____

are bad. Our gang's been counting the _____

and _____ in our sector. Seen any?

YANK - No, hey, there's the _____ and I gotta _____

again.

WHAT TO DO NOW? A TEACHER'S DILEMNA
What Are They Saying

One morning just a few weeks before the date the class was scheduled to go to the National World War I Museum in Kansas City, Missouri, Ms. Browning found a note in her box that caused her great worry. The note said the trip was moved forward one week because of bus scheduling.

"What will I do now," she anxiously asked herself, looking at her lesson plans. "That means five fewer days of class! How will I ever get the students prepared in time?" Sighing, she looked over the schedule, wondering what sections to omit, and what was necessary to present for the students to get the most of their visit. Later that day, she decided to leave "The Story of the Poppy" and "Unknown Warrior" until after the visit.

"Maybe that makes better sense anyway," she reasoned. "Then the students might have a better appreciation of the devastation of the war, both in numbers of dead and wounded and in destruction of towns and farms. Seeing the big artillery and other guns may help them recognize the power of huge guns and the murderous capability of machine guns." So that's what she decided to do, saving also, "The Christmas Ship" story.

After the visit, the class read and discussed all three stories. Instead of taking a test on the unit, as was usual practice, Ms. Browning had the students choose a project. It might be writing a diary such as a soldier kept, or making a sketch or painting of a village or countryside. For others, interested in math, they could graph information about the guns, ships from different countries that were sunk by submarines or numbers of casualties from various armies. Still others could propose their own project, perhaps coming up with some ideas Ms. Browning had not thought of.

She decided this was a better way to evaluate what the students had learned about World War I, and wars, in general. She was curious what her two problem students, Brent and Diaz, would suggest. Maybe they had learned more than she suspected.

World War I airplane aces was the topic today for Ms. Browning's middle school social studies class. Ms. Browning explained that an "ace was a pilot who had downed a certain number of enemy planes. For the French and British, the number was five. For the Germans, who wanted to make the stakes higher, it was eight."

She added, "These pilots became the 'rock stars' of their day. Their names made daily headlines in the newspapers and radio broadcasts. Young people were anxious to get cards showing the faces and flying records of their favorite pilots."

Today the class will read a story about an English boy and his friends who collected and traded the cards. Ms. Browning said, "Turn to page 10 in the booklet. Read the story silently, raise your hand when you finish, and we will discuss the story." The students read:

"William watched through the barbed wire surrounding the grassy field as the Sopwith Camel made a bumpy landing. The jaunty little bi-wing plane hopped a couple of times, then came to a swift halt. The pilot switched off the ignition and pulled himself up out of the cockpit. Stepping lightly onto the wing, he jumped down. His white scarf, still wrapped around his neck, floated in the breeze.

"For two years now William had watched planes take off on their way to France. Sometimes the planes didn't return. William knew there would be an empty chair that night at the dining table where the pilots ate. That meant the pilot was no longer a part of them. This way they honored his death or injuries. But early the next day the young pilots climbed back into their planes and took off for France. There they flew over German trenches, observing movements of both the Allied and German armies.

"Lately, some planes carried bombs which they dropped by hand over certain targets. William knew this from what people told him. The airfield lay next to his family's farm in southeastern England, near Dover. No one from the public was allowed beyond the barbed wire rolls unless they had special permission. But William could see and hear a lot from his position next to the wire.

"As the pilot was climbing out of the plane, the mechanics ran out from the barn. They pushed the plane into the hanger and began the checkup. William knew exactly what they had to do. His father had described how they checked the oil and gasoline mixture, inspected the tires, the wires holding the wings in position, and lots of other things.

"However, his attention was distracted, when at the end of the field, he saw another plane, a French Nieuport, being rolled into takeoff position. The pilot, wearing a similar scarf but heavier, probably made of wool, William decided, ran to his plane. Wool because he may be flying at a higher altitude where the air is cold and the wind blows directly on the pilot's face. The pilot ran to the plane and when it was facing the take-off line, he hopped in.

"That's Billy Bishop, I think," William excitedly said to himself. Sure enough as the plane wobbled near where William stood, he saw the familiar face behind the pilot's goggles. The pilot was of one of his most admired flyers. Bishop, a Canadian, had 65 victories. 'He might be on the way to the 66th,' William thought. 'I wonder where his target is.' "

"The plane took off, climbed rapidly into the clear sky, and disappeared over the horizon.

As William turned to go into his house to wash up for midday meal, some of his friends came running down the dirt road.

" 'Was that Billy Bishop?' they asked. 'We just received some new aviator cards in the mail, and his picture is on one,' Earl said as he proudly held up the card. 'Want to trade? I'll trade Billy Bishop for Germany's Werner Voss and Albert Ball.' "

" 'You must be joking,' William quickly answered. 'That's not a fair trade. Albert Ball is one of England's leading aces now. He's worth a Bishop, all by himself.' The other boys chimed in, saying they had James McCudden of England or Josef Jacobs from Germany for trade. William and his friends argued all the way to the house where William's mother was standing with her arms folded. 'William Ellsworth Woodward, you get in here right now. You are holding up our meal.'

"William told his friends he'd see them before tea time. They could talk more about trades then. Also about the cards of aces printed in Germany that boys over there collected. He wondered what they said about the English aces on the German cards. What a treat to see some of the real cards pictured in the magazine accompanying his cards.

"Then, he thought again about Billy Bishop and remembered the flyer's daring singlehanded raid. It was on a German aerodrome early one morning. Bishop destroyed seven planes on the ground. Then when two other German planes took off to pursue him, Bishop shot them down. Not believing his good luck, he decided it was time to race for his home base.

"But James McCudden of England had some exciting times, and so did Albert Ball. Better hang on to those cards. Captain Ball shot down a well known German ace, Max Immelmann. Later he returned with a wreath of flowers and dropped it on the plane, in respect for Immelmann's bravery and daring flights.

" 'What a fine thing to do,' William thought. He had a card of Roland Garros from France, the idol of all French children. He and an aerobatic pilot, Adolphe Pegoud, also of France, were the world's first two aces. This made them very important. Garros also was the first one to solve the problem of bullets from his machine gun cutting his propeller in two. His idea was to have metal plates attached to the propeller blade so the bullets from his machine gun bounced off.

" 'A smart idea,' William thought. Yes, so smart that when the Germans forced Garros's plane down, he was quickly captured by ground troops before he could destroy his plane. Now the Germans knew his secret. They adapted it to their planes with the help of Dutch inventor, Anthony Fokker. Fokker designed and made airplanes for the Germans. He invented the important 'interrupter gear.' This gear timed the machine gun bullets with the revolving propeller blade, solving the propeller problem. It gave the Germans a distinct advantage over the Allies for several months. Then the Allies captured a downed Fokker and discovered the secret. Soon Allied planes had a form of interrupter gear.

"After eating and helping with the dishes, William had some free time before evening chores. His friends, however, had to work in the fields so couldn't come over. Because most the hired hands went into the army, the families relied upon their older sons to help farm. The boys were paid a small amount so they had some pocket money.

William was lucky today. His dad had weeded the lettuce bed and staked the pole beans yesterday. So William's help wasn't needed today, and he had some free time. He turned to his favorite activity.

"He took his box of cards out of its hiding place in the closet, and spread them out on the bed. The first one was René Fonck of France. William turned the card over and read: "Although only 75 victories were verified, Fonck claimed 142. The real total may be closer to 100." William thought it was a bad idea the pilots had to have three witnesses to claim a victory. He read on: "Fonck had 500 hours of flying time by April, 1917. Twice he shot down six enemy planes in a single day's combat.

"William had heard that 500 hours flying time was unusual. The life of a pilot was the most hazardous of all the military services. Not all the hours were spent in combat. Many hours doing other important tasks like observing the enemy forces and taking photos of the ground activity. William was not discouraged by the possibility of a short life span, and exclaimed.

" 'Wow! That's real flying! That's what I want to do when I am old enough. Turning over the next card, the Frenchman, George Guynemer, was pictured. He was the youngest of all the French aces. In one remarkable encounter, Guynemer was chasing German's Ernst Udet, when he saw that Udet's machine gun had jammed. Udet was pounding on it while still trying to keep his plane in the air. But Udet was unable to clear the jam and was helpless. Guynemer, instead of taking advantage of his handicapped foe, flew his SPAD plane over Udet's Albatros and waved his hand. Then the French pilot headed home.

" 'I wonder what I would have done," William asked himself . After a career of shooting down 54 enemy aircraft, one day Guynemer disappeared on a flight. No one ever found out what happened to him. Neither his body or plane were found. However the French Government rewarded his distinguished flying record with the medal, Croix de Guerre.

"That night he told his father about the encounter between Guynemer and Udet. 'And Daddy, he could have had another victory. It would have been so easy,' William argued. His father responded gently but firmly.

" 'Son, yes, war is about killing people. But there are honorable ways and there are dishonorable ways. I've taught you the honorable way to do things, even though we haven't included flying.' Daddy continued.

" 'It was the same thing with Guynemer and Udet. At that time, Udet was helpless. Guynemer's gun was working, but he chose the right thing to do. That is how I want you to choose." William repeated, 'But to give up a victory so easily!' Then he honestly replied, 'I have to think about it, Daddy.' His father continued,

" 'As for competition, every day we compete with someone or something. We have to in order to live. What is important is how fairly we compete. Have there been times you felt you were treated unfairly?'

"William thought about the card of American Eddie Rickenbacker. He had traded it to Earl for two German aces, Fritz Rumey and Rudolf Berthold. Both had over 40 victories, a high number at the time. Rickenbacker was a new pilot on the scene and had been flying just a few months. His first victory came in April, 1918. Remarkably, only a month later, he had five victories. That meant he was an American ace! William thought about the card the American Eddie Rickenbacker. He had traded it to Earl had heard about the unknown American ace when he made the trade. But William had not.

"Earl was his friend. A Rickenbacker card was valuable now. William should have kept it! This must be what Daddy's talking about,' he reasoned with himself. 'Because we are friends, Earl should have told me before we made the trade. He took advantage of me.' "

"There was no more talk about aces that night. William and his dog went to bed, but not to sleep right away. 'What would I have done?' he asked himself again. Just then William heard the roar of a plane coming in late. It was summer and the sun was just setting, so there was still a little light out for the pilot to see the field. 'I wonder where that pilot has been, I'd like to hear his story,' William whispered to his dog, then fell asleep.

"The next day William had chores to help with until noon,

so he didn't get to see his friends until later. Terry brought two of his new cards. One was Edward "Mick" Mannock, an English pilot who regularly shared victories with other Allied pilots. One such victory was his 61st for which he unselfishly let a new pilot from New Zealand, Donald Inglis, have the credit. Because of Mannock's generous gesture, the New Zealander was able to record his first victory. For Mannock, it was his last act of unselfishness. Later that same day his own plane was shot by a machine gunner on the ground, and Mannock crashed and died.

"The other card portrayed Oswald Boelcke, a German pilot, who studied and used new tactics of air fighting. His tactics included using the position of the sun, altitude, surprise, and turning his plane to meet the pursuer head on. He learned to have the sun at his back whenever possible. Then the other pilot, blinded by the sun, had difficulty seeing where Boelcke's plane was.

"He also hid in vast cloud covers, then dove from the cloud bank to surprise his target. He preferred to fly alone rather than in a squadron. Being alone, he could make the fast turn he was famous for. Sometimes he daringly flew almost up to the other plane as if to collide. Then at the last minute, he would turn and made a quick getaway.

"The thrill of owning a Mannock or Boelcke, or one of the other cards was a challenging decision for William. He sat back and listened to the enthusiastic chatter of his friends. Maybe he would wait until the post man brought his weekly subscription pack of cards.

"Maybe he would get his own Billy Bishop or even the Red Baron, whose real name was Manfred von Richthofen of Germany. The Red Baron often flew an Albatros, the new German plane. None of William's friends had an Albatros, or even a card with the tri-wing Fokker the Red Baron often flew.

" 'That's what I'll do. I'll wait. The postman will be here tomorrow,' " William decided. In the back of his mind he thought about his father's words. Just then the roar of many planes was heard. The boys forgot about their cards as they raced across the pasture to see the Sopwith Camel squadron come flying home. 'I hope they all came back,' William said to his friends, as they counted the planes.

'Eight, nine, ten. Whoopee! that's all of them.'

"The boys cheered as the excited but weary pilots climbed out of their planes. The mechanics ran out to push their planes into the barns to get them ready for the next flight. 'I wonder where they've been. They seem excited about something,' commented Earl. 'Maybe we'll hear about it tonight if we stand by the fence,' William answered. 'I wonder when that new bomber, the Handley Page, will be stationed here,' but the boys were in a hurry to get back to William's house. The bargaining began. 'I'll trade you…' "

The class finished reading the story, so Ms. Browning led with a question: " Why do you think the public was fascinated with the activities of the aces?" Juan raised his hand. "The aces were doing daring things and helping their country win the war."

"And?" she asked. "Anything more to add?"

"Well," he began," We all like to read about what famous people are doing, and these English pilots by shooting down the Germans were making the English feel better about the terrible losses that sometimes their armies suffered."

"What is another issue the story brings up?" Ms. Browning challenged. Immediately Dwon's hand flew up in the air. "I can identify with William about feeling cheated, and it was by a good friend too. It happened to me once, and I've always wondered if that guy was a friend, especially a good friend. But it taught me a lesson. I always find out more before I make a deal."

"Thank you, Dwon, you make a good point about making a deal and what is a good friend. Now tell me, do any of you see another moral problem in this story?" Many hands were raised. "Tricia, what do you think was another dilemna?" Ms. Browning asked. "The incident about the French pilot refusing to shoot the German pilot whose machine gun had jammed. I think I might have taken advantage of his problem with the jammed gun. I'm not sure, but it sure was an easy kill," her voice dropped as she answered.

"How many of you would do what Tricia said she might do?" the teacher asked. About half the class raised their hands. "How many would act like the French pilot?" More hands raised, but some students didn't answer either time.

Trading Cards-
My Ace For Two Of Yours

"Anyone who didn't raise their hand want to tell us why?" Ms. Browning questioned. They shook their heads. "It was an serious commitment then for young men to join the air force. They had heard how dangerous flying was, so literally sometimes a matter of life or death. Most men who volunteered were young and adventurous. Flying seemed so exciting. Also at that age, they felt they were invulnerable. That is typical. But even though some knew the odds were against them, they were excited to climb into that cockpit whenever the signal sounded," she finished.

Seeing signs of confusion, Ms. Browning said, "This appears to be another one of those questions that requires some more thinking. So I'm asking you to write a paragraph stating your position on this matter. If you are confused or not sure, then state the pros and cons. Paragraph due at the end of class."

Ms. Browning wondered if some were too young to make a decision. She decided, it will be only a few years however before some will be making life time choices. She eyed Brent and Diaz, who usually rolled their eyes at a writing assignment, and wondered what they would turn in. Sometimes it was doodling, or maybe just one sentence on the paper.

"Maybe I should check their records and see if they had any problems reading and writing in elementary school." She made a note to herself. "I might try some of those new teaching methods we saw demonstrated in our last workshop." Just then, the bell rang and students started handing in their papers.

NWWI museum archives, Kansas City, MO

S.P.A.D. airplanes like this one fought over the battle lines and attacked the enemy from the skies.

On The Home Front:
Hard Times for an American Family

Ms. Browning began, "Today we have reports on families from three different countries involved in the war. It makes sense to have these reports on the same day so you can compare the hardships the war brought to each family. Civilians of all nations involved in the war experienced 'hard times.' For some, the war caused great suffering, starvation, and the loss of loved ones. For others, the price of war was not as great. Tricia, we will start with you."

Tricia began, "My story is about a family in a middle sized town in America."

"Susie and Roger were arguing over whose turn it was to water the Victory garden when Ma came outside. 'What are you two arguing about now?' she asked, exasperated. Both children answered at once. 'It's Roger's turn.' 'It's Susie's turn to water.'

"Ma replied, 'It's both your turns. Now get the sprinkler can and bucket and get busy. I have to can those vegetables soon, or we won't have any for winter. Most food farmers grow goes to our soldiers in France. You know that, now get started!' she turned and went into the house.

" 'I bet our garden grows more corn and beans than the Smith's,' Roger said. 'Mom's good at canning food so we have almost like fresh vegetables all winter long. I heard the men at the barber shop say that Germans have 'soup lines.' It means people can't buy enough food for themselves, so they have to line up someplace where they cook huge pots of food. Everyone gets some on a plate or in a bowl. I hope we won't have to do that in America.'

'Yes, I know,' said Susie. 'And now Ma's complaining about the shortage of wool. I need a new coat, but wool is rationed, so she's letting out the hem of my old coat. I sure hope the girls won't laugh at how it looks. But maybe their coats have to be let out, too. I don't care too much since all the wool goes to the defense factories so our soldiers will have enough uniforms. I don't want Tim to wear a ragged uniform. He looked real sharp when he first came home. His boots were polished and he was wearing, what were they called? Those things he wraps around his legs and boots to keep water out in case it rains or he crosses a river."

"Roger said, 'You mean puttees.' He agreed that Tim looked like a real soldier and added, 'But I hope he gets his own rifle soon. He needs to learn about shooting it, taking it apart, and how to take care of it. He said America has sent so many rifles to France to use at the front lines, that he has to practice drilling with a wooden rifle. And for gunnery practice, he shares a gun with several guys so each one gets just part of the practice time.'

"Roger continued, "I saved more of my allowance this week so I can buy five victory stamps at school on Stamp Day. I'll be glad when I can fill up a book, like Sally and Charlie down the street. Their Pa is a banker and they get a good allowance. But I can't blame our Pa, he works hard in the munitions plant and gives us what he can. Ma said prices are rising fast. She called it 'inflation.' Even the money Pa makes working overtime doesn't keep up with price increases. I don't understand why this is, but guess I will when I get my own job and money.'

"His voice trailed off as he poured a cup of water on each tomato plant. Susie, who was two years younger, refilled her sprinkler can and started on the row of beans. She wistfully said,

" 'I wonder when Tim gets to come home on his final leave. He's supposed to get some time off before he goes to France. From what I hear, it makes me wonder what the war in France is like. What it's like to hear the noise of the big guns, and see bombs exploding and aeroplanes flying overhead. I'd really like to see an aeroplane someday.'

"Roger also admired their brother, Tim, who was four years older than Roger. "I wonder if they will still be fighting the war when I am 18, so I can join up. Maybe Pa will let me sign up early at 17. Tim says all the soldiers say the war won't last long, once a lot of our American soldiers get there."

"Ma called the children to supper. They wondered what would be missing at the dinner table tonight. On Mondays it was meatless meals. Wednesdays were wheatless, so they used as little bread as possible. Every day Ma tried to use less sugar, and instead, made desserts with honey or molasses.

"Pa commented on how good the Victory garden looked. 'You kids are doing a great job. We're lucky we have a big side yard, and not be like those people in apartments. They have to grow their gardens in vacant lots,' he said. 'Ma, we'll make farmers out of these children yet!' He laughed as he helped himself to more vegetables. 'I miss my meat but guess we can sacrifice some so our Tim gets plenty of good food in the Army.'

"Ma added,' "He writes that he eats like a horse, but they make him practice and drill so hard he hasn't gained much weight. His wool uniform is really scratchy in this warm weather, but fall is coming soon.' Her eyes started to fill up with tears.

"Pa quickly said, 'We know, Ma. Tim gets shipped out in a few months. Now, don't cry, he's going to be all right. I'm proud to have a son in the army.' Just then, Roger spoke up, trying to impress his parents, 'If I were just a little older, I'd sign up. No draft board for me, I'd volunteer. Our teacher has started teaching us lessons about patriotism and helping our country. Helping means even going into the army when we are old enough. We read from a special booklet printed by the government, and it tells us all about being a good citizen. It's neat. We use it every day.'

"Pa smiled. 'Our family is doing its part, son, just you don't get in too big a hurry." Ma answered, 'Yes, we are. There's our Tim, and my two cousins, and your nephew, and three boys in the neighborhood. All in the Army. And none had to be drafted. But they say General Pershing will need as many as 4,000,000 soldiers by the end of next year. That's a lot of men. We'll have over one million in France by the time Tim and his unit gets there. I just hope that doesn't mean you will be working even more overtime, Pa, than you do now.'

"She put her hand on her husband's shoulder as she cleared the table. She was proud of him, but he was getting older and the work was hard physically. Their family included his elderly mother and aunt, who lived with them part of the year.

"Roger spoke up, 'Ma, I have Scouts tonight. We're going to learn how to signal with flags. I can't remember what it's called, but it's important to know, in case we ever get any German spies. You know, like maybe that family Hersbergen down the street. They're from Germany and maybe they have some relatives coming here as spies, and…'

"Ma interrupted. 'Now Roger, I won't have you talking like that. That family has been here for over ten years, and they've never broken any laws, or done anything to hurt the neighbors. Just because they are from Germany, doesn't mean we can be suspicious. Don't go thinking bad things about people who have a German name," she emphasized. Even as she spoke, she wondered if there could be any truth to what Roger had said.

" 'You're right, Ma," Pa added. "At the factory today they fired two men who came from Austria years ago. Said there had been some sabotage with some of the machinery. But they had no proof it was them two fellows. Fact is, I don't believe it was sabotage. That machinery is always breaking down. The boss won't pay to have it fixed right.'

"Susie had finished clearing the table and stacked the dishes in the dishpan. 'Ma, I have my Red Cross knitting class tonight. We're making socks for our soldiers. I don't know if I ever will get the 'knit one, purl two' stitches right. My sock is over a foot long and I haven't even started knitting the bottom part! Maybe I'll start working on the quilts some girls are making to send to orphanages in England. At least I can sew a straight line.' She laughed as she ran out the door just behind Roger.

'Those two children, Ma sighed as she took off her apron. 'Pa, guess we're lucky we don't have bombing raids every night like the newspaper says is happening in London. I don't like shortages of food and rationing and not enough gasoline to drive every day. But you take the trolley and you're working more, and Tim will be in France soon. Yes, I guess we're pretty lucky. I just hope we don't have to cut back on coal for the furnace like we did last winter. It got awful cold on those January nights.' She hung up her apron and sat in her rocking chair. She reached for her knitting basket and took out needles and yarn. Pa opened the newspaper and read the latest headlines.

" 'Women are needed in the tractor factory in town. Now, Ma, I don't want you to go and apply. We could use the money, but a 'woman's place is at home.' And don't you get any ideas like those women called Suffragettes. They think women should be allowed to vote! 'What in the world is coming next?" He folded the paper and went into the kitchen for a glass of water.

"Ma picked up the paper and read the ad: 'Women needed immediately for light work in tractor factory. Good pay, good hours. Apply at the Employment Office. Many openings. No experience needed.'

"She smiled as she knitted. "Hum, many openings, good pay, I'll just check this out. The children are old enough to help me around the house. They'll be all right staying by themselves an hour or so after school. And American women will someday get the vote. Those English women are really working hard on it. We'll see,' she smiled as she knit one, purled two on the stocking for Tim. 'We'll see.'

As Tricia finished, Ms. Browning said, "A good report. And you brought up another important topic. Women getting the vote. At this time not only American women but women in most countries could not vote. Some women in England and America were working on this and were called 'suffragettes.' We'll talk more about this at a later time. Now, we're ready for Franco's story."

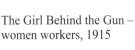

The Girl Behind the Gun – women workers, 1915

free Wikipedia

An English Family During World War I

Franco, who recently moved to the school, announced, "I chose this topic for my report because, even though my first and last names are Italian, I have a great-grandmother who was English. She met my great-grandfather during World War I. He was an Italian soldier in the hospital where she worked as a nurse. After the war, they moved to New York where he had relatives, and that's where I grew up. Here's my story. Some of it I have heard passed down by relatives, some of it I made up."

HARD TIMES IN ENGLAND DURING THE WORLD WAR I

"As Mrs. Thompson cut up carrots and turnips to add to the stew, little Charlie took one look and complained, 'Aw, Mummie, not stew again, especially stew without any meat, and he grumpily walked to the kitchen door.'

"Little Charlie, you know today is meatless day, and if our dear soldiers can do without meat, then certainly we can too. At least the turnips are fresh from the greengrocer and aren't on the ration list. I don't know how I can cook to please all of you. Your sister works the night shift at the munitions factory and can't eat meals with us, so she wants only certain things. Your Daddy is one of the few men tram drivers left, now that most have gone to the service and women are taking their jobs.'

" 'What's this about women taking my job?" Daddy overheard as he came home from work. He hung his driver's cap and jacket on a peg. "Those women out where Sis works are making good pay and part of the profits too. They need workers so bad now," he explained. "Out of 16,000 jobs at the Birmingham Muni, women have taken over 15,000."

"Mummie hastened to defend Sis. 'I know Daddy, but that work is dangerous. Remember the accident last week and seventeen girls were injured? Sis says there was a lot more, but the officials don't want to scare the workers. It's bad enough they come home with yellow faces from the chemicals. She says one smart alec man – he should be at the front he's so healthy – called her a "canary."

Daddy bristled, "I better not hear one of those jacks call my daughter that name or any other! Just because the chemicals make her skin turn yellow, hey, that's a sign of patriotism. I don't like those dodgers who aren't at the front. But giving them a white feather, meaning they're a coward, I don't like that either! It goes against good old John Bull England."

" 'Well, Charlie, at church Parson said those men were 'objectors,' something to do with them being against war of any kind," Mummie tried to remember the words Parson had used. 'Something about not wanting to kill. Parson said those men instead, have to go to prison or work as medics on the front. Parson said we all have to follow our conscience.' "

"Charlie's ears perked up at the conversation between Daddy and Mummie, and he added his bit. 'At school today they were talking about the long list of wounded and dead from the Second Battle of Verdun last week. And they also said that three privates were shot for running away from the battle. That means they were cowards, doesn't it, Daddy?' "

"Daddy thought a minute before he answered. 'Son, they may have just been scared to death. That can be a kind of cowardice, but you know, when you are scared, it's hard to get over that. They say the young man helping at the mechanic's shop on the Green, was discharged from the Army for 'shell shock.'

" 'He just shakes and shakes sometimes and mumbles to himself. Then if someone bangs a tire tool real loud, he runs to the back of shop like he's trying to hide. Once I saw him crying. If he weren't such a good mechanic, he would've lost that job long time ago. We have to be careful how we talk about people. We can't judge them when we don't know their whole story.'

" 'Well, Big Charlie, I believe what Parson says,' Mummie insisted. 'I don't always understand him or remember his words, but he's a good man of the Lord. You can trust him. Like he said when rationing first started, we can do without butter or cheese and margarine. We can find substitutes for sugar.

" 'Just like, before the Americans declared war on Germany, all those merchant ships the Germans sank – well, some of them probably carried sugar from America. I made good puddings then using molasses or honey we got from the peddler. I still make good puddings now although sugar is rationed. You'll agree.'

"Sis came in, ready to get her lunch bucket and go to work. 'What is that outfit you're wearing now, Sis,?' Daddy asked.

" 'It's the new smock and trousers we have to wear when we get up on the cranes in the factory. I got promoted a few days ago. Like 'em?" she asked.

" 'Hum, you're dressed like a man. Now remember, girl, you still gotta behave like the proper English girl you are,' Daddy warned her.

" 'Silly old Daddy, think I'm still a child. I'm doing the work of a man and am proud of it! And one of these days, I'll be getting to vote, like a man!' She kissed Daddy on the bald spot of his head, hugged 'Little Charlie and Mummie and ran out the door to catch the tram.

" 'I don't worry as much about her going to work at night, now that our planes are keeping the bombing raids down. They get up in the air right after the Germans are spotted." Mummie sighed as she stirred the stew and tasted it.

"She continued, 'Those raids were awful. Talk about being scared. First the Zeppelins filling the sky, those 500 foot long monsters. Next it was the Gotha bombers the Germans built because our pilots learned to shoot the Zeppelins down. I think that first Gotha raid last year killed about 95 people. Of course it was near the coast, not London, but it could have been us. Good thing our pilots have those new funny looking little planes, what are they called, Little Charlie? Mummie asked.

" 'You remember, Mummie, they're called Sopwith Camels. Gee, I'd like to fly one of them someday,' Little Charlie answered. 'Oh, I forgot, those lists I saw posted on the store on the way home from school, had names of a lot of men from the next borough. There were old men and women crying and carrying on. One woman fainted, so of course the kiddies with her started bawling. They made a racket.

I'm glad none of our family was in that battle.'

"Daddy spoke up. 'Don't forget, Little Charlie, we've lost two cousins, and your Mum's nephew is listed as missing. Glad I don't have more relatives killed, big as my family is. We've got neighbors and friends, almost everyone in this East End, has lost a family member. We're lucky you're too young and Sis is a girl, though she works a dangerous job.'

" 'You're right, Daddy. And we didn't count two of my teachers. One was wounded badly at Ypres and the other one still missing from Verdun. That was almost two years ago. They should have found him by now, don't you think? And, Mummie, I think it's time for me to be called just 'Charlie,' the boy looked to his parents for their approval.

"Big Charlie ruffled Little Charlie's hair, saying," 'Son, you're big enough now to be called just Charlie." Then he whispered to himself," "Thank goodness, but not big enough to be a soldier." The End.

After Franco finished reading his story, there was silence in the classroom. It was broken when Dwon spoke, "I didn't know the British were bombed in World War I. I thought the planes then were too small to carry bombs."

Dustin broke in, "It wasn't bomber planes at first that did the bombing. It was the Zepplins and other airships. I read about it in a science fiction magazine, only the Zepplins were real. They were filled with helium. That would be scary to be a crew member and know your airship would explode if attacked by gun fire. But I guess it might be scarier to be on the ground with bombs are dropping all around you."

"I read somewhere," Franco explained, "that people took shelter in subways, but I didn't include it because I couldn't find where I had read it. We have to have references, don't we, Ms. Browning?"

"Yes, indeed, and so far all your papers have good references. If you have more questions, please save them until later, so Dwon has time for his report. Thank you, Franco, you did a good job of communicating to us the difficulties and hardships of the English people at that time. Now, Dwon?" Ms. Browning indicated Dwon should start.

A German Family

It was Dwon's turn to read his report. He started out by saying, "I wish I could say I had relatives from England or Germany like some of the rest of you, but you all know my folks came from Africa." The students laughed. "So when I found out no one wanted to report on the Germans, I said, "I'll do it. My folks for a long time have known 'hard times' so we can understand that." He smiled and began reading:

"Wilhelm looked up as his mother came in the door of their two room apartment, took off her coat and wearily sank in her chair. The stuffing in the arms was coming out, and usually she pushed it back under the cloth. Tonight she ignored it, she was so tired. Wilhelm sensed his mother was too tired to care if they ate or not. He asked, 'Would you like for me to set out the bread and some of the soup from last night?'

" 'Oh, Willy, that would be so good of you. We worked two hours overtime again today, and I hurt from my head to my toes." She pulled off her shoes which were cracked at the toes and looked at the holes in her stockings. 'We lost another team today in the bombing of the back building. That means 100 fewer women for tomorrow. Lucky I was in the front yard and saw the bombers in time to run to the cellar. They probably were aiming at the nearby submarine base. Sometimes they hit the railroads down the street where we ship out the ammunition we made.'

"Wilhelm looked startled. He had not heard about today's bombing. At school they never tell the students unless the planes come near the school. Then they all head for the cellars too. His school is near a factory that makes rifles for the war. He hugged his mother in relief that she had been safe.

" 'Mom, do you think the war will be over soon? How much more bombing can we take? The block next to us is completely ruined, and so many families had no place to go. We're down to only two rooms for us now. Do you suppose we'll have to take in a family from one of those destroyed apartments?'

" 'Let's don't talk about the war, son. It's bad enough not

knowing what's happening to your father or where he is. And your brother. He's has been on the missing in action list for six months now. We may never know about him," his mother said, as her voice became almost a whisper.

" 'The last letter from Papa, he sounded so discouraged. Freezing cold, short rations, and no winter boots. Thank goodness, they sometimes have those cubes made of bread that taste sweet. And there's some special food that makes them feel better. He wrote once about a yellow powder that makes pudding when mixed with water. Wish we had some. I really miss those wonderful potato pancakes Oma (grandmother) used to make,' Mrs. Schmidt recalled. Bread made from potato peels, sawdust and dust just didn't take the place of Oma's pancakes.

" 'Do you miss Oma?' Wilhelm asked, knowing he shouldn't, because sometimes she cried when talking about her mother. He knew better to than to ask about Uncle Klaus, her older brother. They hadn't heard from him since he was drafted nearly three years ago. "Oh, yes, my dear boy. Of course I do, but Oma is better off now. She was so sick, and with us having no doctors or medicines, I didn't like to see her suffer,' his mother sadly replied.

"She slowly got up and went to the stove behind her and built up the fire, using a few of the last sticks of wood. She set the fire, and in a few minutes she ladled out the thin pale soup. It contained a few pieces of turnips and cabbage. They sat down to eat. Suddenly they heard the shrill blast of the air raid siren.

" 'Oh no, not again. We're so tired and hungry. Now we've got to go down to the cellar.' Mrs. Schmidt picked up her coat and shoes while Wilhelm got his jacket and a blanket. The cellar was lined with large stones which made it safe, but it was cold and damp. There was no heat in the cellar anyway because of the coal shortage. They barely had enough coal for their small iron stove to heat their two rooms on coldest days. By the time they reached the basement, it was nearly full of people. Young children were crying from the shrill noise of the siren, older women were grumbling about being disturbed at meal time, and the others were scared and talking nervously.

" 'Wonder what 'Tommy's (English pilots) got up there for us tonight?' asked Mr. Herzog, who lived next door to Wilhelm and his mother. 'We'll find out soon enough,' Mr. Schuler answered, then started nodding off, a slight snore now and then.

" 'I don't know how he can sleep through this racket- bombs bursting and children crying. Who knows what we'll find when it's all over,' Mrs. Nagel said in a loud voice to her sister. 'I just hope our bombers hit the Brits in their cities like our Zepplins used to before the Brits learned how to shoot them down. The explosions from the gas that filled those big balloons must have made an fearful sight. And all the 50 or more men in those balloons, what happened to them…' her voice stopped.

" 'Mama, it's so late now, if I'm too tired tomorrow to go to school, can I stay home?' Wilhem suddenly begged his mother. She studied her son's face. This request was unusual for him. He loved school. What was behind it? Was it the talk of the people in the cellar? The bombing raid?

"You're a good student, and my only child left. Hilda died of pneumonia last year when Oma was sick. Your brother, Paul, was killed in the battles in Belgium three years ago." She hugged him until he pulled away from her grasp. 'You'll be all right in the morning, you'll see.' She wanted to hug him again, but something was telling her not to.

" 'Oh, Mom, I miss you so much sometimes, like when I have to stay alone because you're working overtime. Or when the bus drivers go on strike, or the truck drivers strike and block the streets, and it takes you hours to walk home. And this apartment is near another railroad, and it's dangerous for us.'

"Wilhelm felt like crying. But he was a boy and too big a boy to cry, especially in front of his mother and the others in the cellar. Sometimes at night he cried in bed when he thought of all the sadness and troubles brought by the war. He slept on a cot near his mother, and didn't know she could hear him. But she did.

"Finally the 'all clear' siren rang. The exhausted people silently climbed the stairs, glad it was over. They went to their apartments, some saying 'Gute Nacht.' Others waved their hand or tipped their hat to the women. Wilhelm and his mother sat down to the cold soup and munched on dry bread, thinking a little bit of butter would help.

" 'A little bit, just a little bit of a lot of things would help,' Wilhelm said to himself.

"Little did they know that the war would continue almost another year before the Armistice was signed on November 11, 1918 at exactly 11 A.M. During this time, thousands more soldiers would die or be wounded. Thousands of civilians died of influenza and starvation. The British continued their blockade of German ports until the Versailles Peace Treaty was signed in June 28, 1919. The blockade meant no food, medicine or other vital supplies could reach the people. This led to even more hardship for Wilhelm and his mother and millions of other German civilians. The family learned Sergeant Schmidt, father and husband, was killed at the battle of St. Mihiel in September, 1918. A huge force of 650,000 American soldiers led the attack, driving the Germans many miles back. There was never any more word about Hans. He finally was listed officially as "Missing in Action."

"Uncle Klaus had been taken prisoner by the Americans and eventually released in a prisoner exchange several months after the Armistice was signed. He came home to find Wilhelm and his mother in another apartment in a different part of the city. A bomb had finally found the apartment they were living in. Fortunately the cellar was strong, so the residents were spared when they took shelter there during the bombing. But otherwise, the building was demolished. Everyone lost their few possessions, even the iron stoves. Wilhelm and his mother separately shed their tears and expressed their sorrows to others, but kept up a strong front with each other. They were afraid of breaking down completely. This they could not do.

"Uncle Klaus was angry most the time, at the Allies, at his own government, and at the terrible price his family had paid. For what?

He never found an answer. Wilhelm grew up, completed vocation school, and eventually served in World War II. He married and had children, but his mother had died by then and never saw his happiness.

"Today Uncle Klause might be identified as suffering from Post Traumatic Stress Disorder (PTSD). Little was known then about this illness, the words used were 'shell shock.' The End.

When Dwon finished, the class seemed stunned. Disbelief and sadness were reflected on their faces. Finally, Ms. Browning spoke. "I can see this story really affected you. Does anyone want to talk about it?" Silence.

Then Dwon explained," It surprised me that life was so much more difficult for the Germans, and it got worse even after the war. There was great inflation, money almost worthless, the ruling government kept changing, and life was unstable for everybody. And the soldiers didn't get a homecoming parade, it was almost like they had to creep home, no big celebrations. It was terrible." He stopped, almost overcome by his words.

Candi said sympathetically. "They were the enemy of our country and killed our soldiers. But somehow I feel sorry for them. Isn't that strange?"

Ms. Browning asked Candi, "Remind me tomorrow and we will discuss this if you want to. Maybe we all need to think more about it. Class dismissed." Once again, Ms. Browning had her doubts. Are the students old enough to learn about the suffering and horror of the war? They will by their behavior, let her know, she decided.

Explosion at Verdun, 1917

NWWI museum archives, Kansas City, MO

The Christmas Ship

For orphaned European children, Christmas, 1914, was a time they will always remember. This is because thousands of American children and families sent more than seven million gifts of clothing, food and toys on "The Christmas Ship, *Inasmuch*," all the idea of a best-selling romance novelist, Miss Lilian Bell. She had a dream, a vision of this project. To make her dream come true, she rallied her friends, civic groups, churches until finally, all over America and beyond became involved.

From towns large and small, came hundreds of packages. Many of these contained items the children or adults made. This was one of her requirements for the gifts. Woolen factories sent hundreds of caps, scarves and mittens. No gift was too small or large. Even an organ was sent by one generous American.

Getting the gifts shipped to Allied countries was not even a big problem. A wealthy man paid for the services of one of the several ships required to take all the packages. The big problem, Miss. Bell believed, was how to distribute them to orphans in the Central Powers countries and nations invaded by them. This too was more easily solved than had been anticipated. International societies of all sorts offered to distribute them to children in Germany, Austria, Bulgaria, Serbia, France and Belgium. The first three countries were the Central Powers and the last three had been invaded and occupied by the Powers. The societies were helping these people with other services, so they had a system all ready set up to reach the orphans.

The whole project was completed in a matter of months. Miss. Bell's seemingly improbable dream came true. The orphan children of Europe had a Christmas no one imagined could happen.

"Inasmuch"

ANIMALS USED IN THE WAR
Ray's Report on Pigeons

The next day Ms. Browning said, "I think Ray is anxious to give his report, right?" Ray nodded and took his place at the front of the class.

"Mine is about the way the Army communicated with each other by using pigeons. I've always liked birds, my Mom and Grandmother have birds, not pigeons but several other kinds. So when I heard a little about homing pigeons, I was amazed at what they could do. About how they somehow found their way back to their coop. I copied this photograph from one of the books I used." The photo was of a soldier holding a pigeon. "I wanted to get your attention, so I've started my story by using the way the Army assembles its troops and gets their attention." He read: "Atten-hut!"

ATTEN-HUT, COMPANY C

"A voice blared this command throughout Company C of the 316th Infantry, somewhere in France, in late 1917. As the 90 members of the company formed ranks in the center of the reserve area, the captain stepped forward to announce:

" 'This is to inform you that as of 0700 hours tomorrow, we will be receiving a shipment of messenger birds. These messenger pigeons are for military use ONLY. ANYONE harming them in ANY manner shall thereupon be punished. The pigeons will be assigned special handlers to train with the birds. The training area is OFF LIMITS for all other personnel. Any questions, see the sergeant major in charge, Master Sergeant Howard.'

" 'DISSS-MISSED!" roared Sergeant Howard.

"Such might have been the announcement of the arrival of dozens of invaluable little bodies that could fly several hundred miles to their home loft in a matter of hours. In a capsule fastened to their legs were important messages that affected the life or death of many soldiers.

"Pigeons have been used for thousands of years as messengers. At the outbreak of the war in 1914, it was a popular sport to raise and race messenger pigeons in both Europe and the United States. Therefore, some soldiers probably were familiar with the little gray and white birds. The birds had unbelievable stamina and a strong instinct for returning to their home loft. These qualities made them a welcome addition to the American Army. The army was known as the American Expeditionary Forces, or A.E.F. The American troops used pigeons as did all the other armies.

"Within a matter of a few weeks, the pigeons were put into service. Small baskets, each containing two birds, were tied to the backs of their handlers who accompanied troops sent into battle. Baskets accompanied trucks and wagons wherever there was any possibility of being attacked or major problems. Colonels had their staff carry birds when combat was in progress. Several stories tell of colonels themselves releasing birds with urgent messages requesting help or supplies. The response or lack of response could mean life or death to the soldiers.

"Airplanes carried them, dropping them in baskets attached to parachutes with messages into German- occupied Belgium. The Allies needed to know what was happening in different parts of occupied Belgium and depended upon the Belgians finding the birds and sending them with the information. At this time, telephones, radios and even telegraphs were crude and unreliable. Wires and lines could easily be cut, making communication impossible across the miles.

"For the Belgians, finding the bird and sending a message back was done at great personal risk. When the Germans learned about the Allies' use of messenger pigeons, they threatened severe punishment if anyone was found with a bird. The loyal Belgians knew how essential their information was, so they courageously continued to capture birds and release them with the requested messages.

"Pilots also sent messages back to their command posts by the pigeons. The pilots wrote their information on a scrap of paper, then folded the paper into the tiny capsule attached to the bird's leg. The messages gave directions and map coordinates about the enemy's location, as well as the numbers of soldiers. Messages might include number of artillery, direction of troop movements, and overall strength of the enemy force. In the hilly European countryside, such information could not be seen from the ground. It proved to be vital in saving Allied soldiers' lives on a many occasions.

"Small naval vessels and airplanes at sea also carried several coops of birds. One story tells how Pilot's Luck, a pigeon with the British Royal Flying Corps, flew from a downed plane to his home coop. He carried the message, "Airship floundered twenty miles seaward." A patrol boat was sent out immediately speeding through cold, rough waters. When the men in the patrol boat sighted the damaged plane, they sent up a red flare. This was a signal to the airmen that help was on the way.

"The patrol boat reached the downed plane and saw an amazing sight. Six airmen had been in the icy water for eight hours. Still more amazing was one airman who was unconscious, but his frozen fingers still held tightly to the wreckage. The rescuers managed to pull him into the patrol boat, and all six were rescued. They owed their lives to the little pigeon who flew through darkness , high winds and cold temperatures.

"The British government showed their gratitude for this action by awarding seven Victoria Crosses. Six went to the airmen, and the seventh to the little bird, who had that night earned his name, Pilot's Luck. The Victoria Cross is Britain's highest military award.

"In other situations pigeons were sometimes parachuted to British soldiers who were caught behind enemy lines, unable to break through the German forces. The parachute held a basket lined with straw. In it were two birds rolled up in newspapers with only their heads peeking out. Included were a pencil and pad and enough pigeon food for two days. Trapped soldiers often called out, "Soft landing! Soft landing!" as they raced to the baskets.

"Writing out the information requested, they released the birds again in the hope that rescue efforts would begin soon. When a message needed to be sent, usually two birds were released, a few minutes apart. Often enemy snipers would see the first one and shoot it down. In the excitement they might not see the second bird. At times three or four pigeons had to be used if no bird returned with a message.

"Such an occasion happened at one important battle for Verdun in April 6, 1916. Verdun was a crucial French city surrounded by many forts. At Fort de Vaux, the French troops had been holding off German artillery shelling and poison gas attacks for many months. Colonel Silvain Raynal was badly wounded. His soldiers were without food, water and ammunition. He sent off his last pigeon, known only as #787-15 at ll a.m. The bird flew above low lying clouds of gas for 10 miles to his loft. He safely delivered the urgent message.

"Unfortunately, the colonel died before French soldiers arrived to help. The Germans had overwhelmed his troops in a last determined charge. The fort had to surrender. However,in recognition of the colonel's brave defense, the Germans buried the colonel with military honors. As for the nameless little bird, he had made six trips before through gas filled air. On this last trip when he reached his home coop and delivered the message, it was too much. Sadly, the little bird died from his exposure to gas and the exhausting flight.

"The French government recognized both the colonel and the bird with its highest award, the Medal of the Legion of Honor. Also, a beautiful marble statue of a woman with a bird on her shoulder honors all the pigeons that flew in the service of France. The statue is in the nearby town of Lille.

"Many times the birds could fly over the gas which stayed low on the ground. However, for messenger dogs, the gas was too close and they could not avoid contact with it. So a pigeon was used to deliver another urgent plea for help from the colonel of the French 317th Regiment. The Regiment was trapped in a large castle near Vandieres-sous-Chatillon, a village near Reims. This town is in the heavily fought over Marne River area. Germans were surrounding the castle and the situation was crucial.

"The trapped French soldiers had another problem. Prior to this they had captured a number of German prisoners and these were in the castle with the French. This created a potentially dangerous situation. The French feared while the fighting was going on, the prisoners might somehow overcome them. Then the French would have to surrender.

"The colonel sent out his last pigeon, Number #902-15, at 11 a.m. The officer had previously sent pigeons at 6:45 a.m., 7:35 a.m. and 10:10 a.m. asking for ammunition and food. He reluctantly took his last bird out of the basket. It had beautiful white feathers across his back. The colonel had saved this bird until last. He was afraid the gleaming white feathers would make the bird too easy a target. He didn't want to lose the bird, but his situation was desperate. He had to hope the bird would make it through the initial hail of bullets. The colonel had to decide. It was the bird's fate and the colonel's last chance for help, or the fate of his men.

"He decided, and released the bird with its' unusual pattern of glossy white feathers. Somehow the bird made it safely through the hail of bullets to his home loft. In a few hours, help was on the way. A detachment of the French 8th Division fought their way through the German lines to rescue the trapped French troops of the 317th Regiment. Victory was celebrated that night by the troops and their rescuers. Celebrating also may have been the beautiful white feathered bird, known only as "902-15."

"Few birds were given a name. Most of them had numbers which identified where the units they came from. But one heroic pigeon was named after an important American. This big, black male bird was named after his president, President Woodrow Wilson. The bird, President Wilson, was one of the fastest and strongest of all the birds. His actions during many of his flights, earned him much respect. He served with a tank corps at first, then later in the dangerous Argonne sector.

"During one hazardous flight to his loft at Cuisy in the Argonne sector, he flew through a heavy fog. When President Wilson finally landed, it was discovered that he had been badly wounded. But on his leg the message was still securely fastened and legible. Soon help was on the way.

"When his service was over, he was brought back to America and stayed at Fort Monmouth, N.J. where he lived for 11 more years. He died in 1929 and was mounted along with another famous bird,

"Cher Ami." They both are on display at the National Museum in Washington, D.C. in honor of their daring rescues.

"Another nameless but plucky bird was #NU.2709. She flew from the British front trenches in the raging battle known as the Menin Road Battle in Belgium. It was nine miles to her loft. Flying through heavy rain and darkness, she was hit by a machine gun bullet. She fell into mud where she lay all night. By morning she had revived enough to continue to her loft. She died there, but her precious message was found. She has a place of honor in the United Services Museum in London. There she serves as a reminder of the importance of the service of pigeons in World War I.

"It is not known how many pigeons were used by all the armies, but it may have been in the millions. At the beginning of the war in 1914, the Germans seized over one million birds from the Belgians. It was too late for the Belgian king to order all the Belgian pigeons and lofts be destroyed and not fall into the Germans' hands.

"The birds had outstanding performance records. One record shows that pigeons brought messages from 717 airplanes that had crashed at sea. It is estimated that 95% of the pigeons used by the military returned from their missions. No numbers are available on the number of injured or dead. Still, many inspiring and miraculous stories remind us of times they helped countless soldiers to survive and be rescued. The End.

After Chris finished his story, the students had many questions about the birds. Most students had never heard of the birds, or knew the stories. Chris answered as many as he could. But he didn't know how they were trained, or how many pigeons were used and how their homing instinct worked.

Ms. Browning praised the report and added, "You are correct. There are no statistics, and only a few unreliable estimates on number of pigeons used or survived. But many stories exist about Cher Ami, and other famous birds like Spike and Blue Hen, who were not included in the story. You can find their adventures in our school library or the internet," she advised. We continue with Jose's report."

As Jose stood to give his report, he was noticeably nervous. He also had been at the school for only a few months and this was his first time in front of the class. Ms. Browning tried to make him at ease. "Jose, tell us why you selected the horses of World War I as your topic. I imagine you have an interesting reason," she said encouragingly.

"Well, yes, I think I do. I came from west Texas where my Dad worked on a ranch. All us kids got to ride the horses when he could watch us. I grew up on a horse and have a photograph to prove it." He held up a framed picture of a small boy on a large horse.

"That's me, when I was four or five. Anyway, after doing a lot of reading, I made up this story about a horse named Baldy. See the white spot on the forehead of the horse I am riding. That's how he got his name. So I named the horse in my story, 'Old Baldy.' I really miss riding. My Dad says someday we'll move back to Texas, and I can have my own horse. Right now, I just pretend Old Baldy is my horse.

"This story tells about how terrible the war was for the horses, working so hard and with very little to eat at times. Some articles 1 read said that most horses lasted only a few months on the front. If they didn't die from the hard work, then poison gas or exploding shells took care of them. But the horse in my story is different. I made him live through the war. The more I wrote about him, the more I cared for him. I wonder if many soldiers felt that way about their horses?"

The photograph was passed around. Most students had never even seen a real horse, much less ridden one, because they lived in the inner city. The story and the photograph opened a new experience for them. Many envied Jose for his luck having a horse and taking care of it. They wondered if they would ever have that opportunity. Jose began to read:

OLD BALDY – Tale of a Horse in World War I

"They call me 'Old Baldy.' In the Great War I was called 'Bald' for the white spot on my head. I'm 24 years old now, that's why I am called 'Old.' Actually, 24 isn't that old for a horse. I hope to live to be 30 and I'll really celebrate then. But not many horses my age who served in World War One are still around. If the War didn't get them, then the months after peace was declared took its toll.

"After the Armistice, there was hardly any food for horses or people in France, Germany and England. And the pasture and farming land was destroyed by bombing or by tanks and wagons pulled by us horses or mules. Later on, we finally received food shipments from America, my home. Oh, how I miss Iowa, my home state. But you want to hear my war story, so Iowa can wait.

"First, I was a cavalry horse and was trained to make rapid charges. I'd run as fast as I could, our soldiers with their swords pointed forward. Then we heard the clang of swords when we met the enemy. I'd have to stop quickly, careful not to unseat my soldier. He was fighting hand to hand combat and depended upon me to keep him seated.

"These charges were exciting and dangerous. But not as dangerous as when the Germans started using machine guns a few months later. The Germans hid in bushes or the woods, where we could not see them. We'd be advancing, then all of a sudden we heard and felt the stream of bullets whizzing by. Those machine guns can fire up to 600 bullets per minute, and I can't outrun that speed.

"Neither could any other horses. The battle when the Deccan Cavalry from India charged the Germans ended in disaster for the Indians and their horses. The Indians were Sikh warriors whose job from earliest times was soldiering. As usual, they were armed only with long lances. In addition, at this battle, their horses had to run uphill toward the Germans straight into the danger of their machine guns.

"What a tragedy! The Sikhs lost 102 men and 120 horses. The Germans figured out if they aimed at the horse first, then when the horse fell, they could shoot the rider. The Sikhs had no metal head covering for protection because they wore turbans as part of their uniform. It was in their warrior code to never cut their hair or shave their face. Their hair was hidden in turbans that were 30 feet long when unwound. Of course, this meant they needed the help of another person to wind it into a neat turban.

"Although cavalry charges were disappearing from World War I as a military tactic, still some continued to occur during the war. One charge, also resulting in disaster, was made late in the war. It was at a battle in 1918 and occurred when the British hussars charged the Germans. There were 150 horses and riders. Only 4 horses and several riders survived. The British generals had ignored the significant lessons of earlier charges made by cavalry riding against machine guns. It was always a hopeless attack, and resulted in great loss of both men and horses.

"Once my days in the cavalry were over (my commander had learned the foolishness of sending mounted riders against machine guns), I was transferred to Supply. Oh my aching back! It wasn't too bad when all the horses and mules in my section were healthy. But when sickness broke out, the army veterinarians kept those horses or mules in sick quarters. That made us short handed, or could I say - 'short horsed'? I think that's rather funny, why don't you laugh?

"So instead of four horses to a wagon, it might be two. I'm a rather big gelding, 16 hands high (that's 5 1/2 feet tall measuring from the withers. Oh yes, you are asking what are 'withers'? Well, that's above my front leg, the place where the horn of the saddle would be.) I weighed about 1600 pounds, that's when I was young, a two year old. That's when I was sent to France.

"Pulling a wagon was boring except when we had to go to the front lines with ammunition. Sometimes we were hitched to a caisson to pull cannon. The caisson is a wagon that holds the ammunition box. Pulling wasn't so bad, once we found where the road was supposed to be. That was the challenge! I mean, the road had been there. But now it was a mass of mud, churned up by our hooves and the wagon wheels. The marching feet of all the soldiers going up to the front and back made the road even worse.

"One night, when we traveled to the front, it was raining so hard I could barely see ahead. I was hitched to my pal, Blackie, a strong good old pal. My soldier was riding me and leading Blackie. We were always hitched in pairs with one soldier for each pair.

"Blackie and I were going along pretty good as lead horses. Then of a sudden, in the dark, Blackie slipped into a hole. It was filled with mud and rainwater and was so big he couldn't avoid it. Because of the rain, my soldier couldn't see the hole which was on Blackie's side.

"Blackie was panicking. He struck out his front legs and whinnied in fright. The soldiers quickly got some nearby mules also going to the front. Those mules are really strong for their size, I have to admit but ugly looking fellows though, especially compared to Blackie and me. And the noise they made!

"The soldiers hitched the mules to Blackie and tried to calm him down. But he just kept whinnying and kicking the air. The mules were commanded to 'pull.' Blackie calmed down when he heard the command pull." He must have known he was getting help.

"The soldiers also tied ropes to Blackie and they pulled too. Finally with mules and soldiers giving a big heave, Blackie was yanked out of the hole. Everyone gave a big cheer. They had been afraid Blackie was a goner. We've heard lots of stories about horses drowning in deep mud holes. The mud just sucks them down like quicksand, especially if they are frightened and kicked like Blackie did. Wow, was I glad we had help.

"The sergeant come over and unhitched me. 'Baldy, you and Blackie have done your work for tonight. I'm sending you two back to the reserve area to get fed and rested.' It was good news to my ears. They were pointed straight up with fear. Back at reserves we both were washed and brushed and given a bucket of oats. What a treat! I guess I'll have to thank Blackie for the oats. They are so scarce we get them only about once every two weeks. Best of all, I was just glad to have my pal back.

"Another time we had a long march, pulling a 75 mm French cannon with limber and caisson. Altogether it weighed about 6000 pounds. I was straining and just then, I lost a shoe. Now, horses need shoes just like people do. The blacksmith was far away. Besides, we had orders to get that gun in place pronto so our crew could start firing on time. I limped every step. It really hurt. Luckily, we were walking in soft dirt that had no stones.

"After the gun was in place, my soldier took me to the smithy. I hobbled all the way. The smithy quickly saw the trouble I was in. He took lots of time with me and gave me new shoes for all four feet. Said I was due for some new ones anyway. I think he was afraid of another shoe coming off. What a great guy that smithy was!

"Sometimes at night when we were out working, the Germans would shoot flares at us. The flares burst and lit up the ground all around, exposing our position. This way the Germans knew exactly where to aim their guns. Sometimes we managed to get to safety away from their guns. But the flares hurt my eyes long afterwards. Also they terrified me.

"The flares made our work even more dangerous when I was hitched to the kitchen wagon. We had to deliver food to the soldiers in the trenches at nighttime. Sometimes it was completely dark with no moon or stars to guide us. Have you ever stood outside away from streetlights, just no light at all? Then you know what real darkness is.

"The Germans would shoot up flares, trying to find the kitchen wagons. When they spotted us, we were helpless. We couldn't move fast because of all the pots and cans of food. Once our driver had to turn around and find shelter behind a hill. Our men got no food that night. Boy, were they disappointed. I could understand. Sometimes when the hay train didn't come, I had no food either.

"Sometimes horses are wounded and have to lie in 'No man's land' until the bombing and machine guns stop. Then soldiers come find the injured horses. The dead horses have to stay in the field until they can be hauled away by a team of men or animals. Their bodies lying there are bad for our soldiers, creating obstacles for our men when advancing. And the same thing happens if the Germans decide to 'go over the top' of their trenches and attack us. They have to run around the bodies.

"One time I was hurt pretty badly. We were in a 'safe area' behind our guns down in a little ravine. We pulled the gun, caisson and limber and put them in place. Our soldiers led us away from the gun into a ravine. It looked fairly safe. But when we heard the familiar whoosh of a shell, we knew we were in for trouble. Sure enough, it exploded in our midst, killing four of the soldiers and ten of our 18 horses. What a racket there was, shells exploding, men calling for 'help', and horses shrieking in pain and fear. It was terrifying. The shells from both armies continued to boom and whistle in the air.

"Finally the air was silent. The bombardment had stopped. I raised my head and looked at my body. I was shocked when I saw all the cuts from hot shrapnel. I don't know which hurt most, the burns or the cuts. Shrapnel is part of a shell that has metal balls inside. When the shell explodes, little balls come at you from every direction. They get hot as they travel swiftly through the air, and cut and burn, even kill. My soldier later said shrapnel killed or wounded more men than machine guns did. I'm glad I didn't know it that day.

"I lay as still as I could, making a little noise now and then. But I couldn't be sure who was out there whenever I heard movement. I didn't know whether it would be our medics or Germans. When I saw it was our medics, I gave a loud whinny so they would hear me. One medic found me and saw I was injured. He said, 'Big guy. Just stay still. I'll get someone from the vet corps to take a look at you.'

"Soon one of the vet assistants came and checked me over. He asked me if I could get up and walk. I tried to get up, but it took several times with him holding my reins and encouraging me. I hurt all over as we slowly walked and stumbled over large lumps of dirt thrown up by shells. At the vets' tent I was treated and then led to the reserve area. There I was fed oats every day. It was almost worth the pain to get the oats.

"After about a week my soldier came and got me. We were glad to see each other. I nuzzled him on the face, and he laughed. He patted my white spot and my neck. We kept on playing until finally he stopped, put on my old halter and led me back to our tents.

"Then that's when the real troubles began. The convoy of supply trucks coming to resupply us had been bombed by those big large birds in the sky. You know, they make a loud noise when they swoop down on you and bang goes their machine gun. Now they are also carrying bombs. That's really bad news. We were lucky though. Bombs landed all around us but no direct hits. I was really scared but tried my best to stay calm. My soldier stayed with Blackie and me all the time bombs were coming. He could have been killed too. But he knew his job was to stay with his two horses, and he stayed. We were glad he was there.

"Then the rainy season set in. More trucks and wagons nearly always got stuck in the mud. Sometimes they hitched us horses to a truck or an ambulance to pull it out of the deep mud. It was hard on us too. Our feet sank in the mud up to our ankles. I never had to pull so hard in all my life! I didn't know if I could make it, or I would end up in the mud like Blackie.

"And to make matters worse, food was scarce for all of us. No grass anywhere because of the shelling and of course, no oats or hay. That was still on the trucks stuck in the mud. I was supposed to get 14 pounds of hay and 14 pounds of oats, corn or barley every day. Also I was supposed to have salt every third day and plenty of fresh water. I learned not to place much faith in 'supposed to.'

"I was on half rations for weeks, with not even fresh water as often as I liked, unless we were near a stream. It was hard to do my job, I was so weak sometimes. We horses were lucky if we were near a tree or a wagon. Nibbling on the tree truck or the wooden wagon wheel helped fill my stomach, but it didn't give me the energy I needed. A lot of my friends were so weak they couldn't get up. They had to be 'put down,' which meant their working days were over. They had to be shot. I was determined not to let that happen to me. I wanted to return to my home in Iowa.

"When I was taken from Iowa and sent to France, I was one of about one million horses sold to France from America. I remember

Iowa, land of green grass and yellow corn. Oh, how I missed my happy early two years on the farm. My owner was promised I would be sent back after the war, but it didn't happen. I don' know why. Maybe because there were one and one-half million soldiers who had to be sent home from France. Guess there wasn't enough room for both horses and soldiers on the ships after the war ended. Horses had to wait their turn. That meant, we were sold either to French or English officers as a mount, or to a French farm as a work horse.

"It was hard to say goodby to my soldier when his turn came to be shipped out. Would you believe that horses feel affection for the person who takes good care of them? We had had some good times as well as many bad times, but he was always good to me. He never hit me or struck me hard with the whip. He brushed me every day he could. And I had clean water even if it meant he had to walk a long way to a stream.

"1 think it was hard for him to say goodby too. I've heard that if you ask a man who is his best friend, he will say, 'My dog.' But If you ask a horse owner, he will always say, 'My horse.' My soldier and I survived the war together, in spite of both of us being wounded. We were buddies to the end.

"Now 1 belong to an English cavalry officer who bought me when the war was over. He didn't mind my scars from the shrapnel or the occasional limp from that one shoeless foot. He had two young children at home who needed a gentle horse. Every day they come running to find me in the pasture. They pat me on my bald spot and give me an apple or carrot. I prefer oats but don't tell them. I don't want to hurt their feelings.

"They ride me gently, one at a time, led by the stable boy. Sometimes when my back is hurting from old age and the heavy pulling I did in the War, I whinny as the stable boy puts on my saddle. So he makes the riding time shorter that day.

"I'm happy here and lucky to have a good owner. But I miss my soldier and Blackie. I often wonder what happened to them. Were they as lucky as I am?" The End.

Jose paused after he finished, then made a stiff bow. The class broke out in spontaneous applause! Ms. Browning waited until it was quiet, then said: "Jose, I think you have shown us how much you love horses. We all hope someday you will have your own. Now, class, Candi's report."

Soldier with cage of canaries used in tunnels under battlefields.

Extracting a horse which had been blown into the ditch by a shell-burst. Near Reutel, 5th October 1917.

Hi! My Name is Mutt-What is Yours?

Next day it was Candi's turn. She had read a true story about a little orphaned dog in France. Using the facts, she changed the names of the dog and his master and made up the details of the story. She commented, "My dog died recently. I really miss him. I'm glad Mutt found a home with an Army family. That's why I wrote this story." She explained, "The dog is doing the talking." But it was difficult for her to read the story all the way to the end, and she had to stop several times to pull herself together. Here is the story she read:

" 'That young American soldier looks lonely.' I thought. "He's standing in the doorway of that old store. I think I'll go see what's up. Maybe he has some dinner for me. I trotted over to the soldier, barked softly, whined a bit until he looked at me.' 'Hi fella," he said reaching down to pat my head. Just then two other soldiers wearing helmets and a black band around their arms walked up. They were military police, I learned later.

" 'What are you doing out after curfew, Private?' One of them asked in a deep voice. Immediately my soldier saluted and replied,

' "Sergeant, I lost my buddies and can't find the place where we meet the wagon to go back to camp, Sir.' "

" 'Take the first right," the gruff sergeant explained. 'And go on the double. Don't miss this wagon or you'll be in the brig.' They turned and left. My soldier followed their directions, his long legs striding so fast I could barely keep up with him. I had decided this was where I would get my supper. Soldiers always had good food when they were bivouacked in Paris, France, where I lived. So I trotted as fast as I could until we met the wagon pulled by a team of horses. 'Uh, oh, he's leaving without me!' I thought. 'Get in, soldier, we're in a hurry,' came a voice from the driver's seat. My soldier turned to hop on the wagon but my quick two barks made him stop and look at me.

" 'Hungry are you, fella, well up you go.' He picked me up, jumped onto the wagon and hid me under his jacket. Dinner was good that night and the next few nights. During the day I stayed out of sight and didn't bark even though I saw a squirrel scamper up a tree in the camp. At night my soldier (his name was Matthew, I learned), would bring me food and fill my water bowl, an old can. At night I slept with him, snuggled under a warm blanket in a strange shaped thing called a 'pup tent.' Imagine – naming this thing after a dog.

"One day he came running and excitedly told me, 'Mutt (my new name), you and I are going to school – a school for dogs – to become soldier dogs! How do you like that!" I wasn't sure I could be a soldier. How could I carry that heavy gun and wear that funny shaped thing on my head he called a 'tin derby.'

"Matt and I learned together how I would carry messages from one place to another; run the line of the trenches; locate wounded soldiers on the fields at night and bring the medics to get them; and to stand firm during artillery shelling and not be scared by the noise. I was too little to pull carts or sleds. Instead, my small size and fast running made me a great messenger dog. I practiced slipping through the rolls of barbed wire and running around shell holes.

"Learning was great fun but the day came when I had to prove how good a messenger dog I was. Matt and I were with a small advancing infantry group that was cut off by the Germans. The officer wrote a short note about their situation. 'I have 42 men…We are trapped. German machine guns at our rear, front, right and left. Send ammunition.' He fastened it to my special dog collar, and off I ran back to headquarters. Soon help was on the way.

"I did this job many times, and sometimes wore a special gas mask that didn't fit too well when the gas attacks rolled in. I also learned how to warn my men when I heard the artillery shell coming over. My ears were better than theirs, so I would drop to the ground flat with my paws out. Seeing me, they would drop too. Many were saved from the explosions because of my warning.

"I even learned how to salute. I just raised my paw up closer to my head when I saw my soldiers saluting. Then there was the time I proved how tough I was. Twice with my sharp teeth I bit into the legs of two Germans who tried hand to hand fighting with my Matt. My bark and snarl sounded ferocious, and the Germans immediately surrendered.

"The last big campaign was the Meuse-Argonne and as usual, Matt and I started out with the infantry. Several times I carried urgent messages for help. Then on October 9, 1918, Matt and I fought our last fight together. I was starting back with a message about the heavy fog and rough terrain where we were, when the Germans let loose with gas shells. In addition to the gas coming, an artillery shell landed near me. It cut my paw and a piece got in my eye. It hurt and was bleeding, but I kept running until another shell hit nearby. I fell and couldn't get up. A soldier found me and took both me and the message back to the 7th Artillery, where I was headed.

"I was treated for my wounds, but meantime Matt had been severely gassed. When he was brought back to the 7th Artillery on a stretcher, I saw him. I barked and barked, glad he was back. They put me up on the stretcher with him and took us both to the hospital. I got better, but my soldier's condition worsened with the cold French winter. We were both shipped home where Matt remained hospitalized in the Army post hospital. I visited him every day. The army post command made me a dog tag: "1ˢᵗ Division Mutt". The post was my home now.

"I lay by Matt's side day after day, my head on my paws. Sometimes he would wake and lean down to pat me or scratch behind my ears. "Good old faithful, Mutt. I'm trying to get well. Then you can live with me and my family. 'Good old boy.' Then, exhausted he would fall back asleep.

"One day the nurse came, looked at Matt and slowly drew the sheet over his head. I whined. 'What does this mean,' I wondered. She looked down at me, her eyes full of tears, 'Poor Mutt, you've lost your master. He tried so hard to get well.' The doctor came just then and talked to the nurse. They both examined Matt again, but put the sheet back over Matt's head. I whined and the doctor noticed me. He bent down to pat my head.

"I looked into his kind eyes and heard him say, 'Don't you worry, fella, we'll find a good home at the post. Matt was proud of you. It's going to be all right.' And it was.

This is a true story, only the names have been changed. The dog's name was Rags and his master was Donovan. Rags lived with several different families the next 10 years at Fort Sheridan near Chicago. Then he was permanently given to one family who moved several times, always taking Rags with them. He became a military celebrity until he died at age 20 in 1936. He is buried in a pet cemetery near Silver Spring, MD. His gravestone is inscribed: WAR HERO 1ˢᵀ DIVISION MASCOT - WWI 1916 – 1936.

Christina Bersolos, artist

THE AMAZING STORY OF THE SERBIAN BOYS' SURVIVAL MARCH

In fall of 1914, some 20,000 Serbian boys were recruited by the Serbian army as future soldiers and were forced to march with a small military guard almost 400 miles to safety. Fleeing from the German and Austrian armies on the north and the Bulgarian army on the east and south, these boys, ages 12 to 17, were taken from their homes in an effort to save their lives and be useful to Serbia when they were older. Most had never left their small villages before but had lived isolated and primitive rural lives. For about half of them, the strenuous march proved too much. They were unable to make it to safety across the Albanian mountains and rescue by French and British boats.

Fleeing along with peasant families, their carts, oxen and other animals, the boys about half way were unexpectedly left to take care of themselves. The soldiers who had helped to protect them were ordered to return to their units. They had to fight a rear guard action to protect the peasants, the boys and other retreating soldiers.

Through rain, mud, snow and ice, the boys had to depend upon food given by the peasants, if they could not find their own. Their goal was the Albanian mountains, beyond which lay safety. It took eight days for the boys to climb up the mountains and then descend over narrow icy paths into Albanian towns and villages. Sometimes Albanian horse thieves would surprise the boys on the icy trails. The boys constantly feared for their lives because it was only a few years ago Serbia had defeated Albania and claimed it for Serbia. Now was the time for Albanians to take revenge, and they did on the peasants, but not on the boys.

When the remnants of the boys reached Scutari and other Albanian coastal towns, their groups had only half the number that had started. Cold weather, starvation and sickness had taken about 10,000 of them. The tragedy doesn't end here. It is not known if any boys ever rejoined their families. British and French ships, braving the German submarine menace, rescued most of the survivors of the march and took them to places of safety. But finding family members after the war would have been extremely difficult.

The surviving Surbian soldiers, also half in number, recovered their health and fought with the Allies through the rest of the war. They fought despite all predictions that their army had been tottaly destroyed.

It is the boys' courageous story that captures our attention. They are the real heroes. Their youthful struggle to live is perhaps unequaled in history.

Funeral of the Red Baron by Australian troops.

On the way to Verdun. *"They shall not pass"* is the phrase typically associated with the defense of Verdun.

THE BIG DAY HAS COME
Trip to the Museum

The big day had arrived. Ms. Browning's students were finally visiting the National World War I Museum in Kansas City. They listened to the volunteer, Mr. Hancock, give the welcome speech, impatiently shuffling their feet as he droned on. Finally, he led them into the east core of the Museum, where the tour began. There were huge cannons with long barrels pointed straight ahead. Other barrels of gray painted howitzers were aimed up toward the ceiling. One monster cannon was so big, the students wondered how the Museum had managed to get it inside and set into place.

Mr. Hancock, seeing their curiosity, pointed out, "These new kinds of weapons created the death and devastation that made World War I so important in the world's historical time line. The number of deaths of both military and civilians exceeded all previous totals of any war. Total military dead was nine million. Civilian deaths, including those from the Spanish flu, are estimated at 21 million. Some historians estimate as high as 60 million."

He added, "We will talk about eight kinds of weapons that were developed and used in the war. I have a large label taped temporarily on each display case. The weapons are ARTILLERY, SHRAPNEL, MACHINE GUNS, SUBMARINES, AIRPLANES, BARBED WIRE, POISON GAS and HAND GRENADES.

"We will also discuss how a new method of fighting resulted from the efficient killing ability of these weapons. That new way is the dreadful trench warfare. Let's start with ARTILLERY. The students peered around each other to follow his hand as he pointed out certain pieces of artillery.

Mr. Hancock continued, "Because these new weapons had never before been used in combat to any extent, no one could anticipate the terrible results. And it took the commanding officers a long time to change their old ways of conducting a war. This was in spite of the damaging effects made by guns of any size."

He led the group to the large artillery. He continued, "The two largest guns, the Paris Gun and Big Bertha, were so heavy they had to be moved by railroad cars. Fortunately, this limited their use. The

Paris gun had a 91 foot long barrel, which is probably longer than the lot your house is built on. It used a 275 pound shell, the size of an overweight adult male. Another big change was when they invented a method that prevented the gun from recoiling or moving backwards after it was fired. This meant it didn't have to be reset and re-aimed each time. It could fire more rapidly."

"These guns in front of us are huge," Micky thought, but the guns he was talking about, were pictured on a screen above his head. Mr. Hancock pointed them out, saying, "The noise of the oncoming shells over long periods of firing, created nervous reactions for many soldiers. Imagine a loud train coming near your house hour after hour. Would that much noise get on your nerves?" he asked. Some students nodded their heads, trying to imagine the sound.

Leading the group to a display case displaying several shells, Mr. Hancock indicated several different size and shaped shells. Then he walked to another display case. "Here's the shell that really created fear and injury. Now this, the SHRAPNEL – was one of several kinds of shells used in the smaller artillery. The most dangerous was called 'shrapnel,' after the name of the man who designed it. It would explode in midair, showering hundreds of small pieces of hot metal balls. These could injure or even kill a man," Mr.Hancock looked at the students to gauge their reaction. Some looked horrified, others had blank faces. This was beyond their imagination.

They followed Mr.Hancock to other display cases. These contained MACHINE GUNS. Wesley knew about the experimental Gatling gun, which fired repeated shells and made its appearance first in the American Civil War. But he was really interested in the improved machine guns of World War I. He moved up closer to Mr.Hancock so he could see and listen better. "The machine gun was not perfected until it was used in World War I. The Germans had the most effective gun and could shoot down rows of advancing soldiers in a few minutes. This gun also ended the cavalry charges because both men and horses were mowed down."

He indicated the German Maxim guns in the display case.

Some were large and heavy. "This one required four men to carry it and operate it," Mr.Hancock explained. He moved on to point out the British Vickers gun and the French Hotchkiss. Students lagged behind, trying to figure out how the guns operated. They were "water cooled," Mr.Hancock had said. What did that mean? Larry knew that would be one of his first questions when he had a chance. Then Mr.Hancock led the students down a ramp into a space filled with wall charts. There was a huge torpedo and a large mine just past the long barrel of a naval gun.

Leading the students to a chart of Great Britain, the ocean was depicted with hundreds of small painted ships obviously sinking. "Here we find SUBMARINES," Mr. Hancock said. "This underwater weapon also created a shocking sight when it surfaced after torpedoing a ship. Called 'U-boats,' these ships were very effective in destroying the badly needed merchant marine cargo ships that supplied the British and French in 1914-1916."

He pointed too the chart and explained the significance of the tiny sinking ships painted there. Giving the class a few minutes to trade places so all had a turn to see better, he continued. "However, once the United States declared war on Germany in 1917, the merchant marine ships traveled in convoys. These were accompanied by fast moving destroyers and mine sweepers. The losses were then greatly reduced."

Then he pointed up where an AEROPLANE or AIRPLANE was hanging from the ceiling. Su Lyn thought, "A man got into this small fragile thing, and actually flew it!" She shuddered at the thought. Mr. Hancock continued as the students looked upward. Some moved to see the airplane from different angles.

"The airplane made the most improvements and changes of all weapons used in the war. It had been invented in 1903 as a wooden boxlike container that had to be launched. It had no engine and stayed up in the air for only 12 seconds. It covered a distance of only 120 feet. The first successful flight of an airplane with an engine, was made by Wilbur Wright in the same year, 1903. His first flight was for 852 feet and lasted 59 seconds."

Mr. Hancock stopped as students noticed shadows on the floor. "Those shadows represent planes flying," he explained. "You can see some planes swooping down on other ones. When two or more planes were in combat, it was called a 'dog fight.' " Mr. Hancock paused as the two boys who usually snickered at some remark, made their usual noise. Ms. Browning frowned as she moved to stand closer to them.

Mr. Hancock smiled at their behavior but said nothing and ended his talk in this section with: "Several good airplanes, the Fokker VII, Sopwith Camel, and Nieuport, were effective planes by the end of the war. Their usefulness and the damage they could cause to the enemy, made it evident to most military officers that the airplane was here to stay as a weapon of war. You may be interested in this painting of a large 'dog fight.' When 20 planes became involved one day in these fights, the commanders on both sides decided that was too many. So 'dog fights' were forbidden."

He turned to the wall chart behind him showing the Flying Aces of different countries. "Please take a good look at this chart because your time doesn't permit discussion now. I will be glad to answer questions later that I am sure you have."

Mr .Hancock started back up the ramp. He headed to a case filled with different kinds of gas masks. "POISON GAS," Mr.Hancock explained, Allied troops were accustomed to the low lying early morning fogs of northern France and Belgium. One day when they saw clouds that at first were green, then turned yellow, they quickly realized it was not fog, but a deadly gas. They were unprepared and had no gas masks. "Casualties were high. Different designs of masks were tried over time, but no effective one was made until the end of the war."

He paused so the students could take turns seeing the masks and the large photographs of men wearing different models. There were also a dog and a horse wearing gas masks. Then he added, "Because poison gas is breathed in, it either kills the person or causes damage to the lungs.

"The Germans also used at least two other kinds of gas. Mustard gas was the most harmful and fatal if enough was breathed in. It also could be quite painful because it affects the mucous membranes of the body, like the lungs. When gas affects the eyes, it caused blindness, sometimes only temporary. You may have seen photographs of a line of men with their eyes bandaged. Each has his hand on the shoulder of the man in front of him. They had been gassed. The Allies also used gas. Now it is against international law to use it. However, a few nations have since used it, in violation of the law." Ray whispered to Josip, wondering what happened to a country when it used gas in violation of the law.

"That's a good question," Josip decided. "And I want to know which countries used it and when." Retracing his steps, Mr. Hancock crossed over to a display case filled with samples of BARBED WIRE. "These samples are thicker and wider than the barbed wire used on ranches in the United States," he commented, adding, " Large rolls of wire, sometimes eight feet high, were stretched in front of the trenches, making it difficult for soldiers of one army to attack the other side. The wire had to be destroyed by bombardment or cut with large cutters before an advance could be successful."

He indicated the long cutters, some about two feet in length, displayed in the case. He also explained the long screw like metal posts. "These could be screwed silently into the ground so the enemy, if nearby, would not hear any pounding or hammering. The wire was threaded through these posts."

He turned by the end of a display case, and announced, "You will have to take turns coming here to see one of three special exhibits we have. These are called TRENCHES. Ms. Browning, has your class talked about them? They seem well informed so far. They are paying attention and most are taking notes." Ms. Browning answered, "No, we didn't have much discussion and reading, as I didn't have any diagrams I could use. I knew you had examples of the real things here," she explained. "I see you have provided some diagrams of the charts you are describing. I will pass them out while you tell about them."

She began passing the diagrams around so each student had

a diagram to look at. Mr.Hancock asked, "Anyone ever heard of a 'trench?'" Rob raised his hand and spoke up, "Well sometimes the gas company is digging to lay a line in a trench, that's long slit in the ground, but once in a while, the dirt caves in and sometimes a worker is hurt or even trapped. It happened near my house once." "Yes, a modern day example. The trenches in World War I were much larger, big enough to accommodate up to 20 or 30 soldiers sometimes. They were dug into the ground and lined with whatever materials were handy. It could be lumber, small trunks of trees or large branches, among other things. The Germans started building trenches before the War started, so they made them of concrete or concrete blocks with concrete floors. Floors of the French and British trenches, as you will see here, may have been lined with boards. But most of the time it was just an earthen floor. When it rained, and it rained often in Belgium and France where the fighting took place, the trenches flooded. Soldiers might have to stand for several days in the water, never able to dry out their boots and socks. The tops of the trenches often had sand bags piled up in an effort to protect the soldiers from artillery shells and machine gun fire. It was a 'hard and fast' rule to never stick your head above the sand bags. When a soldier did that, he took a great risk in being shot in the head.

"Trenches often zigged and zagged as the diagram shows. This was to confuse the enemy if they ever climbed in the trench. Also it was safer than having one very long trench because the enemy could fire down a straight trench and kill many soldiers. Each trench had a lookout spot called an 'outpost' where a sentry would always be stationed. There were smaller trenches connecting one row with another. They were called 'communicaton trenches.'

"The second row of trenches was a 'reserve zone' in front of third and fourth rows of trenches. "The Germans sometimes had up to six rows of trenches. In some cases a trench had to be dug quickly when troops moved into a new area. The trenches, large and small, wet or dry, were also occupied by uninvited guests known as rats and lice. The rats ate the extra food soldiers were saving, and in general, annoyed the men by running around, especially at night. Some soldiers kept dogs to act as 'ratters,' and tried numerous different methods to get rid of the vermin.

"As for lice, they were very difficult to get rid of because they lived on the body." He stopped to answer Dwon's question. Dwon, puzzled, asked, "How did the soldiers get rid of the body lice? At my old school, we had head check once a month for lice. If the nurse found any, we would have to go home and wash our hair with a special shampoo until the lice were gone." Mr. Hancock smiled, and answered, "At regular intervals, maybe once a month, a similar thing would happen to the troops. They would be taken to 'delousing stations.' Their clothes would be washed, usually by French laundrywomen, and their bodies washed. Then a delousing powder was sprayed on them. But the lice had laid eggs in the seams of the clothing, so even if the uniforms had been washed in boiling water, the eggs survived. The soldiers once again soon would be bothered by the lice.

"In conclusion, trenches were nasty places to be, especially when the enemy's trench mortars were firing overhead. The mortar gun shot a shell making a high arc, then the shell quickly dropped down. The shell was first aimed at the last row of the trenches. Once the desired location was found, it began moving forward, attempting to hit each trench and kill or wound the soldiers in it. Each man dreaded when it was his unit's turn to go up front. It was a miserable time up front either with shelling or with boredom when there was no fighting.

"They had to sleep during the day usually because the Germans preferred to attack at night. It was more difficult for them to be spotted. When it rained, they might be wet for days, Dustin had a question and raised his hand. "How did the soldiers get food, especially if the rats could get into it?" "Good question, young man," Mr. Hancock replied. "Sometimes the soldiers spent hours wondering if the kitchen trucks would get through each night. Their food was delivered only once a day and that was at night. That usually was safest for the kitchen truck, although they had to drive without any lights. The trucks traveled over roads that had disappeared long ago. Instead there were huge pot holes and ruts. Men in the trenches sometimes missed getting their food because of truck mishaps or shelling. When the food did get through to them, it usually was cold, especially the coffee. So they would have to wait until the next night for food.

"The Germans and French each had the help of about 100,000 Chinese laborers in digging the trenches. The Germans had brought Chinese from Tientsin (or Tianjin) China where the Germans had a concession, and the French brought Chinese from Shanghai, the French concession. A concession was a city that the Chinese had been forced to turn over to a foreign Western country. That country was granted a monopoly for selling its products and goods."

Some of the girls whispered to Su Lyn, "Did you know this?" "Shush," she answered, "I'll tell you later." Mr .Hancock was still talking. "Trenches are associated with World War I because of their vast use in France and Belgium. There were over 35,000 miles of trenches along a front fighting line of only 400 miles. For a comparison think about how many miles it takes to circle the earth at the equator. It is almost 25,000 miles. Try to imagine going one and one-fourth times around the earth, and that is the length of all the many trenches added together. Remember, the Germans often had six or more rows of trenches."

He paused, then asked," Now, I would like the next group to come up and see the wall diagram of trenches. Ms. Browning, will you stay with them, while I take the first group to see the French and English trenches? Be sure to have them look at how well the Germans built their trench. This way, boys and girls. I've been told there is a rat in one of them, be sure to see if it's still there," and he led the way among the "oohs and ughs" of some students. After giving the students enough time to be astonished by the trenches used in World War I, Mr. Hancock walked into the adjacent room. Ray had several questions by now. He wished he had time to write them down on his notepad, so he wouldn't forget them. Meanwhile, Mr. Hancock started explaining the next case they saw. "Here we have probably the smallest of all the new weapons, GRENADES. The British called them 'apples' and the Americans named them, 'pineapples'. See how they differ from the older 'potato masher' or 'stick grenade' used first in the war."

Mr. Hancock's hand pointed from one shelf with the smaller grenades to the larger grenades lying on the bottom of the display case. "A man could carry only about six of the stick grenades, but was able to carry 12 or more of the pineapples. And the small grenade was thrown differently, more sideways than overhead. American troops had it easy, because they were used to throwing baseballs, which is the pattern used. All other Allied troops had to give up throwing overhead and learn a new technique.

"Here's a rifle grenade. It's put on a special top attached to the end of the rifle and then fired. It didn't have much advantage distance wise and took longer to prepare. So these weren't used much." He turned and saw a group engrossed at the insignia display. He asked Ms. Browning, "How are we doing on time? Can they take a few minutes to look at some other things they're interested in?" She understood what he meant, and nodded. "Yes, this is a good idea," she acknowledged, "There's so much to see, and they are a curious class."

The class quickly broke up to gather at other display cases. As an aside, Mr.Hancock explained to her, "We're headed into the American section to see the French Renault FT-17 tank. I don't usually have any difficulty getting them assembled for that," he laughed and announced, "Five minutes sharp to look at other cases, then we're heading into something that will really ogle your eyes!" Wesley hurried over to look at German newspapers, Chris and Dustin headed for the rifle display. Both had been hunting with their fathers and were anxious to see what a World War I English rifle, the Lee Enfield, looked like. That would please their dads if they could describe it.

Micky, Jose and Dwon went back to the poison gas display,

arguing about which mask was most effective. Some of the girls including Claudia, Tricia and Candi looked at the French and German uniforms, giggling at the skull's head on the German parade helmet. Darlene and Tricia looked at the display of paper money, surprised by the size of some bills. Other students stood by the huge wheels of some of the artillery. They could barely resist reaching inside the barrel to see what it felt like. A sign, "Please do not touch," restrained them, but the temptation was great. They had heard that the barrels were "rifled" on the inside and wanted to feel what rifling meant.

Just then, Mr. Hancock called them together. "Students, we are going into the American side, and you are going to see a 'Devil's Chariot.' Any one have an idea of what that is? No, well, let's go find out." He led the way to where artifacts from the American army were on display. He stopped at the back of one display. There stood the French Renault FT-17 tank. Mr. Hancock let them crowd up to see better.

He began, "This is, of course, a TANK, a French one. The British developed the first tank, and it was the biggest 'surprise' of the war. The Germans had no idea the British were working on such a machine. A few tanks were introduced in 1916, but unfortunately, the British sent them into battle before many problems had been worked out. So the few tanks were not of much use except to frighten the Germans. Those soldiers had never before seen such a large machine that was moving steadily toward them. They were scared and they had no way to defend themselves. That's why the Germans called the first tanks, the 'Devil's Chariots.' Later the British and French both developed effective tanks which American troops also used. This French Renault FT-17 was one of them," Mr. Hancock finished.

"Now come behind this wall and you can see where the tank was shelled and put out of action. You will also see a representation of a crater in the basement of a farm house that was shelled. This gives you some idea of the size of shell holes that soldiers had to avoid when charging the enemy. Come this way," and he walked ahead. Ms. Browning stayed with the last of the students. Art turned to her, "Gee, Ms. Browning, you were right when you said this war was important. I couldn't imagine it just by reading about it." "Yes," Chris picked up the conversation. "This is really neat. I'm going to be sure my Dad comes down here. He'd like all the guns. Maybe my Mom too. What do you think, Larry?" Larry simply said, "Well, you know what they say, 'Seeing is believing!' " and he followed his class mates around the wall to see the shell hole in the tank and the bombed basement.

Hearing the boys' comments, Ms. Browning found the answer to the question she had asked herself at the beginning of the World War I unit. "I think they are beginning to understand the War, I am pleased. We are fortunate to be able to visit the Museum. This visit seems to be helping them begin to understand war and put its' tragedy into perspective." She smiled again as she approached the two boys about to poke fun at the deep crater. "Be careful, or you'll fall in!" she warned them. "Will these two ever change?" she thought." "No, I guess not."

Wrap Up - Students Discover Meaning of World War I

Big and little boxes, artist tripods, poster board, a contraption made of broomsticks and an oatmeal box were among things the students brought on Wrap-Up Day for World War I. They were so excited that for once Ms. Browning had difficulty getting them quiet. Finally, they laid their equipment in a corner of the room and settled in their seats. Ms. Browning acknowledged their excitement. "I can see you are prepared for another big day. I am anxious also to see what you are going to share with us as an informal review, or Wrap Up, of our study about World War I. We agreed yesterday on the order of presentation, so without any more delay, let's get started. Dwon, you are first."

Dwon brought a chart on which he had drawn bar graphs recording the numbers of men enlisted in the five major European armies, and the numbers of dead, wounded and missing. He selected the armies of Great Britain, France, Germany, Austria-Hungary and Russian because those were the five largest. Then he prepared pie graphs showing those figures in percentages.

Finally he made similar graphs for civilian populations, dead because of injuries or death in the fighting and bombing. He also graphed, where known, the numbers who died of the influenza. He explained, "I like math and big numbers. We rarely use numbers as large as these, that's why I made the charts. I found my information in several books, it wasn't easy, and not all the totals are there.

"For instance, Austria-Hungary and Russia have some totals missing. I indicated this with a star, uh asterisk. Once Russia signed a peace agreement with Germany because of its revolution, no numbers were kept by outside sources. This was really fun, and now I know why big numbers like millions are necessary."

The class applauded and Ms. Browning commented, "Very accurately and neatly done, Dwon. Next, Tricia." Tricia opened her rolled up poster to show it divided into three parts. Each part was labeled either British, French or German. Under the name of each country, there were pictures of pilots. Also a picture of the airplane the pilot usually flew and some hash marks.

"I was very interested in the story, 'Trading Aces' and the various pilots mentioned, so I looked up the top aces from each of these three countries. I also managed to get a picture of the kind of plane they flew most frequently. Each hash mark counts as one plane the pilot has downed. I hardly had enough room for The Red Baron and for Billy Budd, the Canadian ace. They had so many 'kills.' More than 70 each. I have to thank my mom for copying these off the internet for me. By the time she had finished, I knew how to do it. I just hope I don't forget how before my next report is due!" She laughed, the class applauded, and she sat down.

Next was Chris who brought several sheets of paper with drawings of the different kinds of artillery they had seen in the Museum. "I was fascinated by these guns and I copied down all the information about weight, range, size of shell. Also when a gun was developed and which army used them. Lewis machine gun was manufactured in the United States, a similar one was the Vickers in England. These were preceded by the German Maxim gun. I have indicated whether it is howitzer or mortar or cannon and what the gun is primarily used for." He passed the drawings around and sat down to the usual applause.

"Thank you, Chris, I can see how interested you are in your topic. Your drawings are neatly done and labeled." Ms. Browning responded. "Next is Candi." Candi slowly took her place at the head of the class and opened a large sketch book. "I like to draw, and the story of the little dog, Mutt, really made me sad. You know my dog died recently. So I wrote a story about the soldier and his dog, but it's the dog who is injured and dies. My picture shows how sad the soldier is." She read her short story, keeping her tears back and quickly sat down.

"Candi, we are all sorry you are so sad about your dog. Sometime maybe you will write a story about your dog, what you liked to do with him, and how much you miss him. You can either share it with us, or keep it private for only you to read. Your soldier seems sad like you are, and you have transferred his sadness to us as well. Thank you." Ms. Browning seemed a bit sad herself.

Then she brightened up and said, "Time for Brent and Diaz. They asked to do a report together. Boys, please get started." The two boys got the bundle of broomsticks and the oatmeal box and several other items. They set it up to look like an old fashioned movie camera from the World War I time period. Brent explained, "I am pretending to be a camera man from the war. I remember seeing in those large pictures on the wall of the Museum the cameras that were used to make early motion pictures. Only they were made without sound. Diaz is the soldier from the trenches I am interviewing. Our words will be printed on the screen like they used to do in old movies." In the meantime, Diaz had put on a dirty muddy shirt over his clothes, a homemade replica of the tin hat soldiers wore, and strung some water bottles and little bags for ammunition over his shoulders.

They began, Brent: "Soldier, your outfit just came back from the trenches. Would you be willing to tell me about your experiences up there?" Diaz: "I don't feel like talking, I am so hungry, tired and dirty. I just want some peace and quiet, some food and sleep. It was so loud with all the big guns booming every few seconds, Then the spatter of machine guns made us keep our heads down. The Germans attacked every night about the same time. We knew it would be coming, and that made us real nervous. I must have smoked 100 cigarettes the seven days I was up there."

He paused and wiped his face. The two boys continued the dialogue in which the soldier tells of his buddies being wounded or dying, and the one time at dawn when they had to "go over the top." Their story was so realistic, the class and Ms. Browning thought it was a real story, not one they had made up. All the time Diaz was talking, Brent was turning a handle on the oatmeal box which represented the camera. When they finished and bowed to the class, the students burst out in spontaneous applause.

The boys explained how they made up the dialogue by reading letters written by soldiers and printed in several books. They used facts from the letters but changed the circumstances and names. It was time for the bell and Ms. Browning gave instructions for the next day. The students left, some glad their project had been presented. Others were either disappointed the class hour was over, or relieved they had another day to prepare.

Ms. Browning said to herself, "That presentation proves I was all wrong in some ways about Brent and Diaz. It was quite clever and accurate. They must have rehearsed it several times. So what do I do now with them?" She had no time for an answer. The next group of students was coming into the room.

SYMBOLS AND HONORS
The Story Of The Poppy

It was early November. The students walked into Ms. Browning's class to discover a flower lying on each arm of the chairs. Curious, they looked at her desk to find a large vase full of the red flowers, and she was wearing one on her dress. "I see you are wondering why there are flowers on your desks. I want you to take the pin beside it and pin it onto your blouse or shirt. Today is 'Poppy Day.' It is also called 'Remembrance Day' by the English. We used to call it 'Armistice Day', but a few years back, our government decided to honor all veterans of any war the United States engaged in. It is now called 'Veteran's Day.'

"Have any of you heard these names?" she asked. A few students raised their hands. "What do you know about it's beginning?" No one answered. "I thought so. Therefore we are going to watch a DVD about how the poppy became the symbol of World War I. Dustin, you are sitting beside the machine. Will you please start it while I turn down the lights." Ms. Browning adjusted the light switch and the program began. "It was a beautiful spring day in April, 1915, in Flanders, part of Belgium," the voice began. (Scenes of countryside.) "Major McCrae and his assistant were treating the wounded in a field hospital set up on the grass which was slowly turning green." (Images of tables on the green grass. Wounded soldiers lay on them.) The pictures reflected the story as the voice spoke. "The sky was blue, clear of clouds and the usual downpour of rain for once. Bright orange poppies dotted the ground like large handfuls of brightly colored seeds scattered everywhere. Major McCrae was about to remark on the beauty of the day, when the distant boom of German artillery disturbed the peaceful air.

"All of a sudden, he heard the familiar whistle of a shell coming in. The doctor turned to tell his assistant they needed to move the wounded soldier to a safer place. Then the shell landed. It threw up great chunks of brown dirt and stones, covering everything with a layer of brown dirt and pieces of metal.

"The Major looked at his assistant lying on the ground. Fearing he was seriously wounded, Major McCrae checked the pulse at his wrist. There was no response. He examined the man's eyes, laid his ear on his chest, but heard no heart beat. Unbelieving, he saw the stretcher bearers come, lift his friend onto a stretcher, and carry him inside the small building. The flimsy wooden building offered little protection from more incoming shells, but it was the only sheltered place. And that was where the most serious cases were taken.

"Then surprisingly, the bombing stopped as suddenly as it had started. The silence was overpowering, just as the noise of the shells had shattered the peacefulness of the day. 'Hey, doc, you look pale. You'd better rest a minute before the 'meat wagons' come with their next load,' one of the medics advised. Major McCrae sat on a nearby chair, his head in his hands. His mind was whirling, and his ears resounded with the silence of the room. He took out some paper and pen and began to write.What he wrote has been an inspiration for years to millions of people in many languages. It is the stirring poem,

In Flanders Field.

In Flanders fields the poppies blow
Between the crosses, row on row,
That mark our place and in the sky
The larks, still bravely singing, fly
Scarce heard amid the guns below.
We are the Dead. Short days ago
We lived, felt dawn, saw sunset glow,
Loved and were loved, and now we lie,
In Flanders fields.
Take up our quarrel with the foe:
To you from failing hands we throw
The torch; be yours to hold it high.
If ye break faith with us who die
We shall not sleep, though poppies grow
In Flanders Fields.

"In the poem it is the dead soldiers who are speaking. They remind the readers that just days ago they too were alive, seeing the 'sunset glow.' Now their graves are covered with poppies, blowing in the wind. Overhead, the birds still sing even though their song can barely be heard over the sounds of the guns. The dead soldiers challenge the readers to keep fighting the enemy. Otherwise, the dead won't be able to rest under the poppies that 'grow in Flanders fields.'

The poem was sent to England and later published by a newspaper. Many of the readers who were grieving the loss of their sons and husbands, brother and fathers, took comfort from its message. The year of 1915 was the time when England was losing too many soldiers and too many battles. The public felt discouraged and hopeless. The poem's message of hope and it's plea to remember the dead gave the people and the fighting soldiers a reason to carry on. And carry on they did for three more long miserable years until the fighting stopped on November 11, at exactly 11 a.m. in 1918. That's when the Armistice was signed.

"Two years after the armistice in the fall of 1920, an event happened which changed the significance of November 11. Some French ladies came to England with artificial poppies they had made in France. They were sold to benefit the orphaned French children. The ladies met with a committee of British ex-servicemen and showed them the poppies. The committee liked the idea and placed an order for them. The order was for one and one-half million poppies! Over 100,000 pounds (a British coin) was raised from the poppy sale. That is equal to $485,000,000 in today's U.S. dollars. The proceeds went to disabled veterans, who next year made one million more for people to sell.

"Then other countries of Europe started to do the same thing. Poppies grow wild in almost every European country, so the people were familiar with them. This began the custom that has made the poppy become the "universal symbol of remembrance." In 1927 the American aviator, Charles Lindbergh, flew over the American Cemetery at Waregem, Belgium. He scattered thousands of poppy seeds in a sign of our country's participation.

"Waregem is the smallest of the eight American cemeteries in Europe. It is located in Flanders, where the poem was written. A total of 368 American soldiers are buried in the tiny cemetery. They lie thousands of miles from their homeland. On the annual Festival of Remembrance in England, one million poppy petals are released in the air over Albert Hall, a famous building in London. There is one petal for each of the one million dead soldiers of England and the countries that made up the British Empire.

"In America, the day of November 11 has been declared 'Veterans Day.' Servicemen from all the wars the United States has fought in are honored on this important day. This story has been slightly altered from true accounts to make this version. However it is true that Major McCrae did not live to see the end of the war. He died of pneumonia during the last year of the war. His memorable poem still speaks to us almost 100 years later. The account of the selling of poppies and the Festival of Remembrance are from Neil Hanson's book, 'The Unknown Soldiers,' 2007."

Ms. Browning turned off the player and told her class to wear their poppies with pride. Claudia announced, "I'm going to tell my friends in other classes what the poppy means. Ms. Browning, is there a place where they can get some poppies, too?"

"Our principal heard the story and bought a large box full from one of the veterans' groups that sell them each year. I think she would be pleased if students asked her for a poppy. It would be nice for the veterans if you made a donation because they are disabled, but it's not necessary. I'm glad you liked the story. Tomorrow we have another story. This one is about a special ceremony that occurs only on Veterans Day. Class dismissed."

Decorated German officer, circa, 1918

American "Dough Boy", pvt. Bill Lehn, circa, 1918

The Unknown Warrior

In an excited mood, the social studies class of Ms. Browning quickly took their seats. They looked around as if expecting another poppy or something special but found nothing. Ms. Browning noticed this as she called the class to order. "I promised you something special today, and I think you will agree after you have seen the old film I am showing. This was made in 1938 just before the Second World War started and is black and white. It is a record of something else the English people did to honor their soldiers lost in the War.

"It is a copy of an old film. It shows the power of the people, and the ability of a democratic government to respond to their need. In 1920 something special had to be done to honor the loss of 1,000,000 soldiers by this tiny island nation besides selling poppies."

She started the film and the narrator spoke: "One, two, twenty, 100 soldiers buried in one large grave. One large grave, five large graves, fifty, even 100 large graves. All contained bodies of soldiers, some nameless, and all unidentified. They died in the Great War and are buried in France and Belgium. After the war finally ended in 1918, people wondered how to honor their service. How to pay respect? and how to recognize the unrecognizable ones.

"This problem faced the British government in 1920, as the anniversary of the armistice neared. On November 11, at 11 a.m. the signing had taken place in a railroad car in rural France. This would be the second anniversary. What to do? One suggestion was to erect a statue of a famous general. Build a huge monument with 'Unknown Soldier' carved on it.

"To these ideas and others, the people of England, said 'NO.' They wanted a common soldier to be buried in a tomb, one representing all the hundreds of unknown British fallen. A commoner who died for 'King and Country.' Their protests made the government listen, and listen they did."

The film showed groups of people talking, statues of generals, and huge block like monuments as it followed the narrator's voice. "First was the process of how to select a body to be buried. Using a complicated but ultimately fair method, the body was selected. It was placed in a coffin made of English oak, then transferred to England by ship. It was set in a place of honor in Westminster Abbey, England's most important church and guarded day and night by a military honor guard.

"At first, only people with invitations could view the casket, draped with the Union flag. That particular flag had been used on an improvised altar during an important battle in France. Ordinary citizens protested they should be allowed to view the casket too. Again, the people won. For many weeks after November 11, thousands of people passed the casket, paying their respects. No doubt many thought, 'This might be my father or this might be my husband, my brother, my uncle, my son.' Those whose loved one was missing found comfort in passing by the British flag-draped casket. An astonishing thing happened on November 11, when the cathedral's clock stopped chiming the hour at exactly 11 A.M. There was complete silence. Silence among all the crowds. Silence at the train station, the ports, in shops. Buses and trams stopped running. Traffic halted in the streets. All over the little island nation of Great Britain, everyone stopped what they were doing. They were silent for two minutes as each said 'goodby' to the Unknown Warrior.

"This period of two minutes of silence had been planned, but no one knew if it would happen. It did. Imagine a nation of 80 million people coming to a complete stop for two minutes in 'The Great Silence' as it was later called. No phone calls were made. Courts stopped their trials. No doctors performed operation in hospitals, but instead bowed their heads in respect. Factories were silent as workers stood by their machines.Pilots shut off the engines of planes on the ground at airports. Even ocean liners on the seas stopped their engines. All the British world was silent for two minutes.

"As someone later said, 'The dead lived again.' Such was the first honoring of an Unknown Soldier. The practice of honoring one common soldier was adopted also by France in 1920. Belgium and Italy a few years later followed with similar ceremonies. Then other nations adopted the idea.

"In 1921 the American government was persuaded to honor its unknown soldier. A splendid ceremony was held with speeches, marching bands and awarding of medals to veterans and important generals. Large crowds cheered. Everywhere there was excitement. The moment was full of emotion as people remembered those men who were missing. For the American Unknown Soldier, there were only a simple inscription identifying him, 'An Unknown American who gave his life in the world war.' There was the same Great Silence of two minutes as in England.

"After the burial of the American Unknown Soldier in Arlington National Cemetery, near Washington, D. C., the honor guard fired a 21 gun salute. This means the guns fire 21 times.This salute is an honor reserved for the highest officials, including presidents and kings or heads of other countries.

"Meanwhile in England, the Great Silence continued every year for 19 years until the outbreak of World War II in 1939. Such was the enormity of grief of the English people. With this ceremony people in countries all over the world recognized the sacrifice of a soldier whose body is unidentified. A soldier who has no grave of his own. His body may be unknown to man, but as the words reassure us, he is 'Known (only) to God.' A body that represents the three million unidentified soldiers who died in The Great War." The film came to an end and its loose end flopped until Ms. Browning caught it.

The class was silent as she removed the reel and put it in the canister. She asked, "Any comments?" Finally Candi raised her hand. "I didn't know about this, it makes me sad for all those families. Three million, did I hear that correctly?" she paused. Jose said, "I saw a statue of a soldier in a little Texas town. It was in the courthouse yard. It said 'In memory of all the soldiers in World War I,' but it didn't mention any unknown soldier. Do we have them for other wars?" Chris answered, "In Washington, D.C. where I went to visit my grandmother, she took me to see a lot of monuments. I liked the Vietnam Memorial best. It was long and made of black marble with all the names of the dead engraved. It was neat, well, I mean, it impressed me."

Ms. Browning smiled at his choice of words. "Yes, there are memorials for unknown soldiers from each war we have fought since. They also are buried in Arlington Cemetery. Well, this finishes our unit on World War 1, at least in the classroom. I hope you will continue to think and learn about other wars our country has participated in. But I hope you will remember how pivotal, that is, how things 'pivoted' or changed since that time. How life for just about everyone in the world changed drastically, or at least was never the same. We start a new unit tomorrow, 'The Great Depression.' Class dismissed." As the students

filed out, Ms. Browning observed that they had learned answers to many questions they had started with. And, she smiled, she had found a few answers to her questions. This made teaching so rewarding and exciting.

What! You wish that I was home?
So do I. But not before
We have beaten to the door
All the huns that're in the war.
Take this little tip from me,
Home is great;
So is Liberty.

Post Card, circa, 1918

SHORT, SHORT STORIES
Chivalry in the Air

British and French pilots practiced the art of chivalry towards their enemy. This means that they acted in a generous and courteous manner most of the time. This included the act of flying back over the site where a pilot lay after being shot down, flowers were dropped over the site. Such famous pilots as the Red Baron even earned a military funeral by the British and Australians, since he was shot down over their territory.

One day, Albert Ball, the British flying ace, discovered that Max Immelmann, the German flying ace, was in a nearby field. He flew over the trenches in the field and dropped a note to Immelmann, challenging him to a duel at two o' clock that afternoon. He swore that the British anti-aircraft guns would remain silent and trusted that the German guns would do also. At two o' clock, all the guns were still. British and German soldiers watched breathlessly as the two aces fought to the death. Immelmann's plane went down, and as his body was being removed from the wreck, Ball released a huge wreath of flowers to pay tribute to the gallant airman. He later himself was shot down.

Bourke, Joanna. An Intimate History of Killing: Face-To-Face Killing in Twentieth-Century Warfare. New York: Basic Books, 1999. Print.

Buried with the Germans

The father of Albert Ball, British ace who was killed, purchased the field in France where his son's plane crashed and Ball died. He is buried in Annoeullin Communal Cemetery and German Extension. He lies among German soldiers, the only British serviceman in the entire cemetery.

Q1182, Crown Colpywright, Imperial War Museums

How to Capture Subs

In the Allies' struggle against the dangerous German submarine, they used strong nets made of wire cables. These were stretched across harbors and bays. Some were even used in open waters where it was likely a submarine would be passing by. If the sub's propeller became caught in the net, the submarine had to return home for repairs.

In addition the Allies placed mines near the nets. The mines exploded when the submarine touched it. Allied patrol boats watched for signs of the U-boat (the German name for submarine) such as ripples in usually calm waters, or movement of the nets, and of course, explosions of the mines.

A Faithful Dog

A dog known as Red Cross No.19874 protected his German master's grave long after the German sergeant died and was buried near old Chateau Fere in France. The sergeant was part of the German High Command which had moved out because the Americans were on the way. An American sergeant found the dog lying across the grave of his master. The dog growled and showed his teeth to the American. However, it was obvious from his starved and weakened condition he could not put up much of a fight.

The American knew that, but he respected the dog's loyalty to his buried master. The dog wore the German Red Cross harness, a flask on one side of his neck and a first aid kit on the other. It took three days before the dog responded to some food the American pushed toward him. Finally he decided he could trust the Americans. He let them take him to the Army vet where he was treated and recovered. The fate of the dog is unknown, but it is hoped he found a good master to live with.

GENERAL PERSHING AND THE AMERICAN ARMY

Once American declared war on Germany, President Wilson selected General John J. Pershing to command the American forces in France. A veteran of several previous U.S. wars, General Pershing was faced the with difficult task of raising an army from the existing professional army of about 130,000 men. In less than two years he created, supplied and trained an army of more than 4 million men. He accomplished what was an amazing, almost impossible job.

Photo courtiesy of General John J. Pershing's Boyhood Home.

Even more difficult was his assignment to convince the French and British allies that Americans would fight only as an American unit and only under the American flag. The Allies had lost millions of men during the war and were desperate to fill in the ranks of their depleted armies. But Pershing and President Wilson knew that if the United States was to have a seat at the peace treaty table, they had to prove their army was a first class fighting force. The Allies exerted constant pressure on General Pershing for over a year. It was not until May, 1918 when they finally agreed to his demands.

Once General Pershing doggedly won his point, the American First Army was formed and immediately went into action. Their first major offensive was the St. Mihiel salient in southern France which the Germans had occupied for three years. With an army of 650,000 and combining the planes of the Air Force and the tank corps, General Pershing within a few weeks pushed the Germans out of the salient.

Then the Americans were asked to take on the Meuse-Argonne sector, another large battle. This required Pershing's staff to plan two major offensives in about two weeks' time. Because of the high quality of his staff, this was accomplished. Amercan troops became successful despite high losses due to their inexperience in fighting and lack of training.

Within a few more weeks, the Germans were asking for surrender terms, and the war ended on Nov. 11, 1918 at 11 a.m. The Allies claimed victory, largely in part due to the stubborn position of the American general and the enthusiasm and fighting spirit of the many American troops.

Some years later Congress awarded General Pershing the title, "General of the Armies." No American general since George Washington had ever received that designation. Many military writers and historians claim that General Pershing is America's greatest general.

GLOSSARY

Aces - A pilot who had shot down the number of enemy planes required by his country. France and Britain required five and Germany required eight.

Ack Ack - Anti-aircraft

Aerial torpedoes - A mortar bomb with fins dropped from an aircraft

Aeroplane - The first spelling of "airplane"

Alleyman - Nickname for a German

Ammo - Ammunition

Archibalds - Anti-aircraft artillery or fire

Ashcans - Heavy German artillery shell

Bevo - A lieutenant, not experienced or competent

Big Bertha - One of two German largest guns, range of 72 miles

Blighty One - A wound severe enough requiring the soldier to be sent to a hospital behind the lines or even to England to recuperate

Boocoo - French "beaucoup" meaning a lot of, much or many

Bully beef - Canned corn beef was the main protein ration for British army.

"Canary" - Slang word used by British to describe girls and women who worked in munitions factories. The chemicals made their skin turn yellow.

Casualties - Can refer to dead or wounded soldiers. A count is also kept of "missing" and "taken prisoner."

Deep Sea Turkey - Salmon issued as rations; a large supply meant monotonous diet.

Dog biscuit - Hard tack

Doughboy - American soldier, comes from 1846 when some soldiers found flour and rice and mixed it with water to form little "doughboys" which were baked in ashes of the fires

Firestep - A step built into each trench, two or three feet from the trench floor, allowing a soldier to peer over the side of the trench to see the enemy's trench line

Flying bedstead - An early clumsy but stable airplane

Fritz - Another nickname for German soldier

Galloping goose - An airplane making a clumsy or awkward take off

German Empire - Consisted of the Pacific islands of Western Samoa, Marianas, the Caroline Islands and the Marshalls; also in Africa Germans controlled Namibia (South West Africa); Ghana (Togolands); Cameroons (Kamerun); East Africa consisting of Tanzania, Rwanda and Burundi; and Chinese concession city of Tsingtao.

Gold fish - Canned salmon

Gotha - A very large German plane with four engines that bombed England many times

Handley Page - First effective bomber developed by British, carried 16 bombs weighing 112 lbs. each; went into action in November 1916 with the Royal Navy Air Service. Wings could be folded up to fit into hanger.

Kite balloons - Observation balloon anchored to a cable on the ground

Parson - A minor English clergyman

Pup tent - Tent shared by two soldiers

Pump handle - Salute a higher ranking soldier

Rain in the face - The brimless overseas cap

Red lead - Catsup

Red legs - The red stripe on outside seams of artillery trousers in late 1800s

Rookies - A new recruit or replacement

Stand to - Time when front line troops were required to man the firestep of their trench, fully armed in case of enemy attack. Took place at dawn and twilight when attacks most likely to occur.

Stick bombs - German hand grenade with long wooden handle for throwing

Ticked off - Scolding or reprimand

Tin cows - Canned condensed or evaporated milk; highly popular at the front

Tin Lizzie - Steel helmet worn by British or American soldiers

Tommie - Nickname for British soldier; came from sample application form used for enlistment. It used the name "Thomas" as an example.

Toot pronto - At once; French for "toute de suite"

Top - The Top Sergeant; highest ranking sergeant

Trench foot - A fungus infection of the foot which can be infected with gangrene. Can be serious. Is caused by constant exposure to moisture and cold air from the soldier staying in a trench for long periods of time without drying out or warming feet.

Typewriters - A German machine gun (making a noise like an old typewriter)

Undercarriage - Legs of either a man or woman

Wurst - A German observation balloon; is shaped like a sausage

Yanks - Nickname for American troops; comes from "Yankee" possibly Yankee Doodle Dandy"

Zeppelin - A 500 foot long balloon, could stay in air for eight hours, dropped bombs on London and Paris causing much damage and civilian deaths. Was filled with helium and if caught on fire, would explode and burn.

BIBLIOGRAPHY

Adams, Simon. Eyewitness World War I. London: DK Publishing, Inc. 2001.

Banks, Arthur. Military Atlas of the First World War. South Yorkshire: Pen and Sword Books, 2001.

Becker, Jean-Jacques. The Great War and French People. Warwickshire, UK: Berg Publisher, 1983.

Bell, Lilian. Story of the Christmas Ship. Chicago: Rand McNally & Company. 1915.

Brown, Malcolm. The Imperial War Museum Book of The First World War. London: Pan McMillan. 2002.

Bull, Stephen. Battle Tactics: Trench Warfare. Haverton, PA: CASEMATE. (NO DATE)

Campbell, Christopher. Aces 7 Aircraft of World War I. Dorset: Blandford Press, 1981.

Churchill, Allen. Over Here. New York: Dodd, Mead and Company. 1968.

Connelly, Sean. Witness to History. World War I. Chicago: Heineman Library, 2003.

Cothun, Marion B. Pigeon Heroes. Birds of War and Messengers of Peace. New York: Coward-McCann. 1944.

Gilbert, Martin. The First World War. New York: Henry Holt and Company. 1994.

Glandfield, John. The Devil's Chariots. Gloucestershire: Phoenix Mill. GL52 BU. 2001.

Gordon-Smith, Gordon. Through the Serbian Campaign. London: Hutchinson & Co. 1916.

Gray, Randall and Argyle, Christopher. Chronicle of First World War, Vol. 1, 1914-1916. London. Butler and Tanner, Ltd. 1990.

Gray, Peter and Thetford, Owen. German Aircraft in First World War. London: Putnam, 1962.

Hanson, Neil. Unknown Soldiers. New York: Vintage Books, 2007.

Harper's Pictorial Library of the World War. Lowrie, Rebecca Lawrence, Ed. New York: Harper & Brothers Publishers. 1920. Vol. XI. A Child's Book of the War.

Hughes, Matthew and Philpott, William J. The Palgrave Concise Historical Atlas of the FIRST WORLD WAR. Trowbridge, Great Britain: The Cromwell Press. 2005.

Jarymowycz, Roman. Cavalry from Hoof to Track. Mechanicsburg, PA: Stackpole Books. 2009.

Jones, Fortier. With Serbia Into Exile. New York: Grosset & Dunlap. 1916.

Keegan, John. An Illustrated History of the First World War. New York: Knopf. 2001.

Kennedy, Over Here. New York: Oxford University Press. 1980.

Kennett, Lee. The First Air War, 1914-1918. New York: the Free Press. 1991.

Lighter, Jonathan. The Slang of the American Expeditionary Forces in Europe, 1917-1919: An Historical Glossary, Chapel Hill, N.C.: Duke University Press. 1972.

Meyer, G.J. A World Undone. The Story of the Great War 1914-1918. New York: Bantam Dell, 2007.

Nicolsen Juliet. The Great Silence. Great Britain: John Murray, Publishers, Hackette UK Company. 2009.

Persico, Joseph E. Eleventh Month, Eleventh Day, Eleventh Hour. New York: Random House Books, 2004.

Sasse, Fred. Rookie Days of a Soldier. St. Paul, MN: G. W. Greene,1924.

Schaeffer, Christine K. The Great War. A Guide to the Service Records of All the World's Fighting Men and Volunteers. Genealogical Publ. Co. 1998.

Q1408, Crown Colpywright, Imperial War Museums

Mules to water, Amiensw-Albert Road, October, 1916

INTERNET SOURCES

INTERNET SOURCES:

agrinews.com. <u>Food will win The War: Minnesota Crops, Cooks and Conservation during World War I</u> (book review).

<u>Aircraft of World War 1. The Fokker Scourge.</u> http://en.wikipedia.org/wiki

<u>The Early Year of Military Flight. A Short History (click to Chpt. 1).</u>http://www.raf.mod.uk.hist.

<u>The Effect of World War 1 on Children in the United States.</u> http://en.wikipedia.org/wiki/

<u>Food will win The War: Minnesota Crops, Cooks and Conservation during World War I</u> (review of book which chronicles Minnesota food growing.) agrinews.com

<u>The Gotha Raids.</u> German Strategic Bombing during World War 1. http:www.historylearningsite. co.uk/rationing and world+war one.htm.

<u>Home Front Civilians. World War 1 Gardens:</u> Patriotism and feeding families; also Blood-thirsty Huns; anti-German hysteria swept through American Homefront. (brief articles.)
   http://firstworldwar.cloudworth.com/home-front.ph

<u>Infantry weapons in World War One.</u> historylearningsite.co.uk.

<u>Rationing and World War 1.</u> http://www.historylearningsite.co.uk/rationing and world war I. htm.

<u>Serbian Soldiers, Names of.</u> http://en.wikipedia.org/wiki/Category: Serbian soldiers.

<u>The Aces of World War 1.Trading cards.</u> http://www.century-of-
   flight/new%20site/framesWW1/520aces frame.htm.

<u>The Model 1917 U.S. Enfield.</u> htttp://www.amercanrifleman.org/m-articlepage. aspx?id+4232&cid+1.

<u>World War I.</u> http:en.wikipedia.org/wiki.

<u>The Wright Brothers-First Flight, 1903.</u> http:www.eyewitnesstohistory.com/wright.htm.

At date of printing, these sources were valid.
The author apologizes if any difficulty due to change of site occurs.

Russian prisoners of war who escaped from the Austrians during the advance. Italian Front.

Q26754, Crown Colpywright, Imperial War Museums